AN INTRODUCTION TO
MATHEMATICAL MACHINE THEORY

This book is in the
ADDISON-WESLEY SERIES IN
COMPUTER SCIENCE AND INFORMATION PROCESSING

DEAN ARDEN AND RICHARD VARGA
Consulting Editors

AN INTRODUCTION TO
MATHEMATICAL MACHINE THEORY

by

SEYMOUR GINSBURG

Senior Mathematician

System Development Corporation

ADDISON-WESLEY PUBLISHING COMPANY, INC.

READING, MASSACHUSETTS · PALO ALTO · LONDON

To
Little Ellie
and
my parents

PREFACE

Since the pioneering work of Huffman [H2]* and Moore [M3] in 1954, a considerable mathematical literature has arisen about the behavior of data processors from the point of view of terminal characteristics, that is, input sequences versus output sequences. This book is intended as an introduction to selected topics from this literature, in particular, those with which I am most familiar.

Attention is focused on three types of "machines." These are the sequential machines of Huffman-Moore-Mealy, the abstract machines of the author, and the tape-recognition devices popularized by Rabin and Scott. Turing machines have been omitted deliberately. To include them would (i) detract from a presentation of material whose source is a situation in data processing and (ii) result in the addition of a large amount of extra text. The interested reader will find a most lucid treatment of Turing machines in Davis [D1].

There are four main chapters and an introductory one, Preliminaries. Chapter 1 deals with *complete* sequential machines. The main topics considered are (i) equivalence of states and its relation to reduction, and (ii) the problem of subjecting a known machine in an unknown state to a sequence of inputs to determine the final state by the resultant output sequence. Chapter 2 concerns *incomplete* sequential machines, in particular, the reduction of superfluous states and general synthesis. Chapter 3 deals with *abstract* machines. Many examples related to data processing are given. Equivalence of states, equivalence of inputs, and synthesis from the inputs are discussed. In the final chapter tape recognition devices are considered. The automaton and various extensions of it are discussed. Also studied are regular sets and their relevancy to recognition devices.

This book is developed from a set of lecture notes for a course taught at the University of California at Los Angeles and the System Development Corporation during the three years 1960–1962. These classes consisted of (i) programmers with an interest in the theoretical aspects of data processing, (ii) curious mathematicians, and (iii) computer logical designers with an interest in the more abstract phases of their art. It is not surprising, therefore, that this text has been written with these three groups in mind. The mathematical maturity needed is the ability to follow elementary (but not necessarily simple) set-theoretic arguments. A knowledge of data processing is not needed except for certain examples occurring in Chapter 3.

---

* Numbers in brackets refer to the bibliographical references at the end of the book.

I am indebted to the students of the aforementioned course whose zealous questioning and classroom discussions added much to the readability and accuracy of the text. I am grateful to the System Development Corporation for providing typing and duplicating services. Finally, I should like to thank the Addison-Wesley Publishing Company for suggesting that this material be made available in book form.

S.G.

Santa Monica, California
May, 1962

CONTENTS

PRELIMINARIES

Some set-theoretic concepts and properties to be used in later chapters are here reviewed. It is suggested that the reader omit this material and, instead, refer to it as needed.

The set of those elements having a property P is written as $\{x|x$ has property $P\}$.

The set with no elements in it, called the *empty set*, is denoted by $\emptyset$.

For two sets A and B, A is a *subset* of B, written $A \subseteq B$, if each element of A is an element of B. A is a *proper* subset of B if A is a subset of B and there is an element of B which is not in A.

Two sets A and B are *equal*, written $A = B$, if $A \subseteq B$ and $B \subseteq A$.

The set *union* of a family $\{A_\alpha|\alpha\}$ of sets, written $\cup_\alpha A_\alpha$, is the set of elements in at least one of the A_α.

The set *intersection* of a family $\{A_\alpha|\alpha\}$ of sets, written $\cap_\alpha A_\alpha$, is the set of elements which are in all of the A_α.

If there is only a finite number $A_1, \ldots, A_n$ of sets involved, then the set union is written as $A_1 \cup A_2 \cup \cdots \cup A_n$, and the set intersection as $A_1 \cap A_2 \cap \cdots \cap A_n$.

Two sets A and B are *disjoint* if $A \cap B = \emptyset$.

The number of elements in a set A is denoted by $\#(A)$.

Given two sets A and B, by $A - B$ is meant the set of those elements in A which are not in B.

If A is a subset of B, then the *complement* of A with respect to B is the set $B - A$. The act of taking complements is *complementation*.

A *family* of sets is a set of sets.

A family $F = \{A_\alpha|\alpha\}$ of subsets of a set A is a *Boolean algebra of sets* if F is closed under set union, set intersection, and complementation (with respect to A). That is, if C and D are elements of F, then $C \cup D$, $C \cap D$, and $A - C$ are elements of F.

For any two sets C and D which are subsets of A,

$$C \cap D = A - [(A - C) \cup (A - D)]$$

and

$$C \cup D = A - [(A - C) \cap (A - D)].$$

Thus a family of sets which is closed under complementation and under either set union or set intersection is closed under all three operations. Therefore a family of sets is a Boolean algebra if it is closed under complementation and under either union or intersection.

1

If A is a set, then the family of all subsets of A is denoted by 2^A. 2^A is a Boolean algebra of sets.

The *Cartesian product* of a sequence of sets $A_1, \ldots, A_n$, denoted by $A_1 \times \cdots \times A_n$, is the set of all n-tuples $(a_1, \ldots, a_n)$, where each a_i is in A_i.

A *partition* of a nonempty set A is a family $\{A_\alpha | \alpha\}$ of nonempty pairwise disjoint sets such that $\cup_\alpha A_\alpha = A$.

A partition $\{A_\alpha | \alpha\}$ of a set A is a *refinement* of a partition $\{B_\beta | \beta\}$ of A if each A_α is a subset of some B_β.

Two sequences $I_1, \ldots, I_r$ and $J_1, \ldots, J_s$ are *equal* if $r = s$ and $I_i = J_i$ for each i.

A finite sequence $I_1, \ldots, I_k$ is frequently written without commas, that is, as $I_1 \ldots I_k$.

If $J = I_1 \ldots I_k$ is a finite sequence, then by $(J)^n$ is meant the sequence

$$\overbrace{I_1 \ldots I_k I_1 \ldots I_k \ldots I_1 \ldots I_k}^{n \text{ times}}.$$

In particular, letting J be a sequence of length one, say $J = a$, it follows that

$$(a)^n = \overbrace{a \ldots a}^{n}.$$

A *relation* R between a set A and a set B is a subset R of $A \times B$. If (x, y) is in the relation R, then it is written as $x \, R \, y$ or $x \, R \, y$ holds. If $x \, R \, y$ does not hold, then it is written as $x \, \not{R} \, y$.

A *relation on a set* A is a relation between A and itself; i.e., it is a subset of $A \times A$.

Two relations between A and B are *equal* if they are equal as subsets of $A \times B$.

A relation R on a nonempty set A is an *equivalence relation* if (i) R is reflexive, i.e., $x \, R \, x$ for all elements x in A; (ii) R is symmetric, i.e., if $x \, R \, y$ then $y \, R \, x$; and (iii) R is transitive, i.e., if $x \, R \, y$ and $y \, R \, z$, then $x \, R \, z$.

If R is an equivalence relation on the set A, then each set $[x] = \{y | x \, R \, y\}$, where x is in A, is an *equivalence class* generated by R.

If R is an equivalence relation on A, then the family of equivalence classes generated by R is a partition of A.

An equivalence relation R is of *finite index* if R generates only a finite number of equivalence classes.

A *labeled, directed graph* is a triple $(V, E, \{A_e | e \text{ in } E\})$, where V is a nonempty set whose elements are called *nodes*, E is a set of ordered pairs of nodes whose elements are called *directed edges*, and each A_e is a set of symbols called the *label* of the edge e.

A *function* (or *mapping*, or *transformation*) is a triple (A, B, f), where A and B are nonempty sets and to each element x in A there corresponds an element, denoted by $f(x)$, in B. (A, B, f) is also called a function f of A into B.

A function (A, B, f) is usually denoted by the symbol f and is said to be *defined* on A.

If (A, B, f) is a function and $\{f(x)|x$ in $A\} = B$, then f is said to be a function of A *onto* B.

A function f is *one-to-one* if $f(x_1) \neq f(x_2)$ whenever $x_1 \neq x_2$.

Let (A, B, f) be a function. If (C, D, g) is a function such that $A \subseteq C$, $B \subseteq D$, and $f(x) = g(x)$ for all x in A, then g is said to be an *extension* of f.

Let (A, B, f) be a function and C a subset of A. Then (C, B, g) is said to be a *restriction* of f to A if $g(x) = f(x)$ for every element x in C.

A set A is *denumerable* if there exists a one-to-one function f of A into the set of positive integers. A is *denumerably infinite* if it is denumerable and infinite.

A set is *nondenumerable* if it is not denumerable.

If a denumerable number of elements is removed from a nondenumerable set, then the resulting set is nondenumerable.

A *semigroup* S is a set of elements H, together with an operation $\circ$ on H, such that

(i) $a \circ b$ is in H for each a and b in H,

and

(ii) $(a \circ b) \circ c = a \circ (b \circ c)$ for all a, b, and c in H.

The symbol $\circ$ and the parentheses are omitted whenever possible.

A subset A of a semigroup S is a *generating set* (for S) if to each element w in S there is at least one finite sequence of elements $w_1, \dots, w_r$ in A such that $w = w_1 \dots w_r$.

An element a of a semigroup S is an *identity* element if $ax = xa = a$ for every element x in S. There is at most one identity element in a semigroup.

Let Σ be a nonempty set. The set of all nonempty sequences $I_1 \dots I_r$ of elements in Σ, under the operation of concatenation, i.e., $I_1 \dots I_r \circ J_1 \dots J_k = I_1 \dots I_r J_1 \dots J_k$, is a semigroup, called the *free* semigroup (generated by Σ). The set $\theta(\Sigma)$ of all sequences, both empty and nonempty, of elements in Σ, under the operation of concatenation is a semigroup, called the *free semigroup with identity*. (The empty sequence ϵ is the identity element.)

A semigroup S is said to satisfy the *left cancellation law* if for all elements a, b, and c in S, $ab = ac$ implies that $b = c$.

Each free semigroup satisfies the left cancellation law.

Let G and H be two semigroups. A function f of G into H is a *homomorphism* if $f(xy) = f(x)f(y)$ for all elements x and y in G. If, in addition, f is a one-to-one mapping, then it is said to be an *isomorphism*.

An equivalence relation R on a semigroup S is *right invariant* if $ac\ R\ bc$ holds for all elements c in S whenever $a\ R\ b$ holds.

The definition of *left invariant* is similar.

An equivalence relation on a semigroup S is a *congruence* relation if it is both left and right invariant.

Given three integers k, m, and n, by $k \equiv m \pmod{n}$ is meant that $k - m$ is an integral multiple of n.

CHAPTER 1

COMPLETE SEQUENTIAL MACHINES

Modern technology has produced a multitude of devices which have inputs, internal configurations or states, and, in some sense, outputs. Mathematical machine theory studies models of axiom systems encompassing these three items. In this book we investigate a number of such models which bear upon some aspect of a data-processing system.

In this chapter a class of machines is considered whose outputs depend on the sequential history of the inputs. That is, the present output depends not only on the present input but also on the previous inputs and the order in which these inputs appeared. Further, these devices have a finite number of inputs, a finite number of internal configurations, and a finite number of outputs. These machines, as all machines considered here, are deterministic in nature, so that if the input history is repeated, the output history is repeated. Besides data processors, other examples of such machines are safes, vending machines, and sequential switching circuits.

1.1 Preliminary concepts. We now introduce the complete sequential machine and two ways of representing it, the δ, λ matrix and the state graph.

Definition 1.1. A *complete sequential machine* is a 5-tuple $S = (K_S, \Sigma_S, \Delta_S, \delta_S, \lambda_S)$, where

(i) K_S is a nonempty finite set of "states,"

(ii) Σ_S is a nonempty finite set of "inputs,"

(iii) Δ_S is a nonempty finite set of "outputs,"

(iv) δ_S is a function (called the "next-state" function) which maps $K_S \times \Sigma_S$ into K_S, that is, $\delta_S(q, I) = \bar{q}$, where q and $\bar{q}$ are in K_S and I is in Σ_S; and

(v) λ_S is a function (called the "output" function) which maps $K_S \times \Sigma_S$ into Δ_S, that is, $\lambda_S(q, I) = E$, where q is in K_S, I in Σ_S, and E in Δ_S.

The subscripts on K_S, Σ_S, Δ_S, δ_S, and λ_S are omitted whenever S is understood. Thus $(K_S, \Sigma_S, \Delta_S, \delta_S, \lambda_S)$ is frequently written as $(K, \Sigma, \Delta, \delta, \lambda)$.

5

Unless otherwise stated, in this chapter the term "machine" or "sequential machine" is to mean "complete sequential machine."

It is convenient to describe a particular machine by a "δ, λ matrix" (also called "flow table" [H2]*), which is a table having the form shown in Fig. 1.1. Each box in the figure has both a δ-entry and a λ-entry, with the δ-entry to the left of the λ-entry. The machine described in Fig. 1.1 is $(K, \Sigma, \Delta, \delta, \lambda)$, where

$$K = \{q_1, \ldots, q_n\},$$

$$\Sigma = \{I^1, \ldots, I^a\},$$

$$\Delta = \{\lambda(q_i, I^j) | 1 \le i \le n, 1 \le j \le a\},$$

and δ and λ are the functions defined for each state q and each input I.

EXAMPLE 1. Let S be the machine in Fig. 1.2. Then S is the 5-tuple $(K, \Sigma, \Delta, \delta, \lambda)$, where

$$K = \{q_1, q_2\},$$

$$\Sigma = \{I^1, I^2, I^3\},$$

$$\Delta = \{0, 1, 2\},$$

$$\delta(q_1, I^1) = \delta(q_1, I^3) = \delta(q_2, I^2)$$

$$= \delta(q_3, I^3) = q_1,$$

$$\delta(q_1, I^2) = \delta(q_2, I^1) = q_2,$$

$$\lambda(q_1, I^1) = \lambda(q_2, I^2) = 0,$$

$$\lambda(q_1, I^3) = \lambda(q_2, I^1) = 1,$$

and

$$\lambda(q_1, I^2) = \lambda(q_2, I^3) = 2.$$

The usual interest in a physical machine is in its response to a sequence of inputs. In order to study this behavior, we now extend the two functions, δ and λ, so that for each (empty) sequence of inputs $I_1 \ldots I_k$, called a *tape of length* k (*length* 0), and each state x, $\delta(x, I_1 \ldots I_k)$ is the state at which the machine terminates and $\lambda(x, I_1 \ldots I_k)$ is the resulting sequence of outputs.

---

* Numbers in brackets refer to the bibliographical references at the end of the book.

	I^1	$\ldots$	I^j	$\ldots$	I^a
q_1	$\delta(q_1, I^1)\lambda(q_1, I^1)$				$\delta(q_1, I^a)\lambda(q_1, I^a)$
$\vdots$					
q_i			$\delta(q_i, I^j)\lambda(q_i, I^j)$		
$\vdots$					
q_n	$\delta(q_n, I^1)\lambda(q_n, I^1)$				$\delta(q_n, I^a)\lambda(q_n, I^a)$

FIGURE 1.1

	I^1		I^2		I^3	
q_1	q_1	0	q_2	2	q_1	1
q_2	q_2	1	q_1	0	q_1	2

FIGURE 1.2

Definition 1.2. For each tape $I_1 \ldots I_k$ and each state x, let

$$\delta(x, I_1, \ldots I_k) = \delta(x_k, I_k),$$

where $x_1 = x$ and $x_{i+1} = \delta(x_i, I_i)$ for $i \geq 1$; and let

$$\lambda(x, I_1 \ldots I_k) = \lambda(x, I_1)\lambda[\delta(x, I_1), I_2 \ldots I_k].$$

Let $\delta(x, \epsilon) = x$ and $\lambda(x, \epsilon) = \epsilon$. Clearly $\epsilon = $ empty sequence

$$\lambda(x, I_1 \ldots I_k) = \lambda(x, I_1)\lambda(x_2, I_2) \ldots \lambda(x_k, I_k).$$

The situation in Definition 1.2 may be represented pictorially as follows.

$I_1 \qquad I_2 \qquad \ldots I_k$

$x_1 \qquad x_2 \qquad \ldots x_k \qquad x_{k+1}$ terminal state

$\underbrace{\lambda(x_1, I^1) \ \ \lambda(x_2, I^2) \ \ldots \lambda(x_k, I^k)}_{\text{resulting output sequence}}$

EXAMPLE 2. Let S be the machine in example 1. Then

$$\delta(q_1, I^1I^2I^1I^1) = q_2 \qquad \text{and} \qquad \lambda(q_1, I^1I^2I^1I^1) = 0211.$$

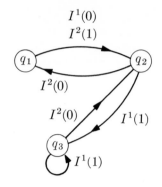

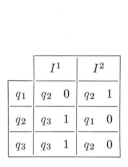

	I^1		I^2	
q_1	q_2	0	q_2	1
q_2	q_3	1	q_1	0
q_3	q_3	1	q_2	0

FIGURE 1.3

FIGURE 1.4

	I^1	
q_1	q_2	0
q_2	q_3	0
q_3	q_4	0
q_4	q_1	1

FIGURE 1.5

	I^1		I^2		I^3		I^4	
q_0	q_0	0	q_1	0	q_1	0	q_1	1
q_1	q_0	1	q_1	0	q_1	0	q_1	1

FIGURE 1.6

The calculation of $\delta(q_1, I^1I^2I^1I^1)$ and $\lambda(q_1, I^1I^2I^1I^1)$ is shown pictorially below.

$$I^1 \quad I^2 \quad I^1 \quad I^1$$

$$q_1 \quad q_1 \quad q_2 \quad q_2 \quad q_2$$

$$0 \quad 2 \quad 1 \quad 1$$

EXERCISE 1.   Let S be the machine in example 1.   Determine

(a) $\delta(q_2, I^1I^2I^2I^1)$,   (b) $\lambda(q_2, I^2I^1I^2I^2)$,   (c) $\lambda(q_1, I^2I^1I^1I^2I^3)$.

EXERCISE 2.   For each state x, each tape $I_1 \ldots I_k$, and each integer r, $1 \le r \le k$, show that

(i) $\delta(x, I_1 \ldots I_k) = \delta[\delta(x, I_1 \ldots I_r), I_{r+1} \ldots I_k]$,

and

(ii) $\lambda(x, I_1 \ldots I_k) = \lambda(x, I_1 \ldots I_r)\lambda[\delta(x, I_1 \ldots I_r), I_{r+1} \ldots I_k]$.

One way to represent a sequential machine is by a δ, λ matrix. Another way is by a labeled, directed graph called the *state graph* G_S (or *transition diagram*). Specifically, let S be a machine whose distinct states are $q_1, \ldots, q_n$. The nodes of G_S are n abstract elements named $q_1, \ldots, q_n$. For each ordered pair of (not necessarily distinct) states q_i and q_j, G_S has a directed edge (q_i, q_j) if and only if there exists an input I such that $\delta(q_i, I) = q_j$. If G_S contains a directed edge (q_i, q_j), then the label of this edge is

$$I_1\big(\lambda(q_i, I_1)\big)$$
$$\vdots$$
$$I_k\big(\lambda(q_i, I_k)\big),$$

where $\{I_1, \ldots, I_k\}$ is the set of those inputs I for which $\delta(q_i, I) = q_j$.

EXAMPLE 3. The state graph of the machine in Fig. 1.3 appears in Fig. 1.4.

EXERCISE 3. Draw the state graph of the following machines:

(a) a *mod 4 counter* (Fig. 1.5),
(b) a two-input full-serial *adder** (Fig. 1.6),
(c) a three-bit *shift left register* (Fig. 1.7).

	I^1	
q_0	q_0	0
q_1	q_2	0
q_2	q_4	0
q_3	q_6	0
q_4	q_0	1
q_5	q_2	1
q_6	q_4	1
q_7	q_6	1

FIGURE 1.7

1.2 Equivalence. The purpose of physical machines is to perform work of some kind. We now study the question of work in sequential machines without defining the term "work" itself. We shall regard the relation of the input sequences to the output sequences, that is, the terminal characteristics, as the manifestation of work done by a state in a machine. We shall define when two sequential machines are to be considered equivalent from this point of view. Then we shall exhibit a finite procedure for finding a smallest-state machine equivalent to a given one.

Definition 1.3. Let S and T be sequential machines such that $\Sigma_S = \Sigma_T$. A state p in S is said to be *equivalent* to a state q in T, written $p \equiv q$, if $\lambda_S(p, J) = \lambda_T(q, J)$ for every tape J.

Equivalent states may be regarded as doing the same work when measured by terminal characteristics.

---

* For this machine it is customary to write 00 for I^1, 01 for I^2, 10 for I^3, and 11 for I^4.

	I^1	
p_1	p_1	0
p_2	p_1	2

FIGURE 1.8

	I^1	
q_1	q_2	0
q_2	q_1	0
q_3	q_3	1

FIGURE 1.9

EXAMPLE 1. Let S and T be the machines in Figs. 1.8 and 1.9, respectively. Then $p_1 \equiv q_1$.

From Definition 1.3, it immediately follows that (i) $p \equiv p$ for all states p; (ii) if $p \equiv q$, then $q \equiv p$; and (iii) if $p \equiv q$ and $q \equiv r$, then $p \equiv r$.

Among the states of a particular machine, $\equiv$ is an equivalence relation.

Lemma 1.1. Let S and T be sequential machines. Let p in S and q in T be equivalent states. Then $\delta_S(p, J)$ and $\delta_T(q, J)$ are equivalent states for every tape J.

Proof. Let J_1 be any tape. Since $p \equiv q$,

$$\lambda_S(p, J) = \lambda_T(q, J) \quad \text{and} \quad \lambda_S(p, JJ_1) = \lambda_T(q, JJ_1).$$

Then

$$\lambda_S(p, J)\lambda_S[\delta_S(p, J), J_1] = \lambda_S(p, JJ_1)$$

$$= \lambda_T(q, JJ_1)$$

$$= \lambda_T(q, J)\lambda_T[\delta_T(q, J), J_1]$$

$$= \lambda_S(p, J)\lambda_T[\delta_T(q, J), J_1],$$

whence $\lambda_S[\delta_S(p, J), J_1] = \lambda_T[\delta_T(q, J), J_1]$. Since J_1 is arbitrary, it follows that $\delta_S(p, J) \equiv \delta_T(q, J)$.

We now formulate a definition of the conditions under which two machines are to be considered the same when measured by terminal characteristics.

Definition 1.4. The sequential machines S and T are said to be *equivalent*, written $S \equiv T$, if for each state p in S there is a state q in T so that $p \equiv q$, and, conversely, for each state q in T there is a state p in S so that $q \equiv p$.

FIGURE 1.10   FIGURE 1.11

EXAMPLE 2. The machines in Figs. 1.10 and 1.11 are equivalent.

Clearly the notion of equivalence between machines has the three properties: (i) $S \equiv S$ for each machine S; (ii) if $S \equiv T$, then $T \equiv S$; and (iii) if $S \equiv T$ and $T \equiv R$, then $S \equiv R$.

Definition 1.3 (equivalence between states) includes the phrase "... for every tape J." Since there are an infinite number of tapes for every machine, the definition is not finitary in nature. The purpose of the ensuing theory is to describe a finite procedure that determines exactly those pairs of states which are equivalent.

Notation. Let S be a sequential machine. For each integer $k > 0$, let $\overset{k}{\equiv}$ be the relation defined by $x \overset{k}{\equiv} y$ for states x and y if and only if $\lambda(x, J) = \lambda(y, J)$ for every tape J of length $\leq k$. Clearly $\overset{k}{\equiv}$ is an equivalence relation. Denote by P_k the set of equivalence classes generated by $\overset{k}{\equiv}$.

EXERCISE 1. Show that $x \overset{k}{\equiv} y$ if and only if $\lambda(x, J) = \lambda(y, J)$ for every tape J of length k.

In view of the above exercise, it is sufficient when dealing with $\overset{k}{\equiv}$ to consider only tapes of length k. This is frequently done in the sequel.

The basic results about the relation $\overset{k}{\equiv}$ and the partition P_k are summarized in the next lemma.

Lemma 1.2. (a) $x \overset{k+1}{\equiv} y$ if and only if $x \overset{k}{\equiv} y$ and $\delta(x, I) \overset{k}{\equiv} \delta(y, I)$ for every input I.

(b) If $P_{k+1} = P_k$, then $P_k = P_j$ for every integer $j \geq k$.

(c) If $P_{k+1} = P_k$, then $x \equiv y$ if and only if $x \overset{k}{\equiv} y$.

(d) If $\#(P_1) = 1$, then $P_2 = P_1$.

✓ (e) If $n = \#(K_S) \geq 2$, then $P_{n-1} = P_n$.

Proof. (a) Suppose that $x \overset{k}{\equiv} y$ and $\delta(x, I) \overset{k}{\equiv} \delta(y, I)$ for every input I. Let $I_1 \ldots I_{k+1}$ be any tape of length $k + 1$. By assumption,

$$\delta(x, I_1) \overset{k}{\equiv} \delta(y, I_1).$$

.

Then

$$\lambda[\delta(x, I_1), I_2 \dots I_{k+1}] = \lambda[\delta(y, I_1), I_2 \dots I_{k+1}].$$

Since $x \overset{k}{\equiv} y$, it follows that $\lambda(x, I_1) = \lambda(y, I_1)$. Then

$$\lambda(x, I_1 \dots I_{k+1}) = \lambda(x, I_1)\lambda[\delta(x, I_1), I_2 \dots I_{k+1}]$$

$$= \lambda(y, I_1)\lambda[\delta(y, I_1), I_2 \dots I_{k+1}]$$

$$= \lambda(y, I_1 \dots I_{k+1}).$$

Thus $x \overset{k+1}{\equiv} y$.

Now suppose that $x \overset{k+1}{\equiv} y$. Clearly $x \overset{k}{\equiv} y$. Given an input I, consider the states $\delta(x, I)$ and $\delta(y, I)$. Let J be any tape of length k. Since $x \overset{k+1}{\equiv} y$, then $\lambda(x, IJ) = \lambda(y, IJ)$, that is,

$$\lambda(x, I)\lambda[\delta(x, I), J] = \lambda(y, I)\lambda[\delta(y, I), J].$$

Since $x \overset{k+1}{\equiv} y$, it follows that $\lambda(x, I) = \lambda(y, I)$. Thus

$$\lambda[\delta(x, I), J] = \lambda[\delta(y, I), J].$$

Hence $\delta(x, I) \overset{k}{\equiv} \delta(y, I)$.

(b) Suppose that $P_{k+1} = P_k$. By induction, suppose that $P_{k+i} = P_k$ for $i \le m$, where $m \ge 1$. To show that $P_{k+m+1} = P_{k+m}$, whence $P_{k+m+1} = P_k$, it is sufficient to show that if $x \overset{k+m}{\equiv} y$, then $x \overset{k+m+1}{\equiv} y$. Therefore let x and y be any states such that $x \overset{k+m}{\equiv} y$. By (a), $x \overset{k+m-1}{\equiv} y$ and $\delta(x, I) \overset{k+m-1}{\equiv} \delta(y, I)$ for every input I. Since $P_{k+m-1} = P_{k+m}$, then $x \overset{k+m}{\equiv} y$ and $\delta(x, I) \overset{k+m}{\equiv} \delta(y, I)$. By (a), $x \overset{k+m+1}{\equiv} y$.

(c) Let $P_{k+1} = P_k$. If $x \equiv y$, then obviously, $x \overset{k}{\equiv} y$. Suppose that $x \overset{k}{\equiv} y$. By (b), $x \overset{m}{\equiv} y$ for every integer $m \ge k$. Thus $\lambda(x, J) = \lambda(y, J)$ for every tape J, so that $x \equiv y$.

(d) Suppose that $\#(P_1) = 1$. Then each state is $\overset{1}{\equiv}$ to every other state. Thus, for all states x and y and all inputs I, $x \overset{1}{\equiv} y$ and $\delta(x, I) \overset{1}{\equiv} \delta(y, I)$. Then $x \overset{2}{\equiv} y$. Therefore $P_2 = P_1$.

(e) Suppose that $\#(P_1) = 1$. By (d), $P_1 = P_2$ whence $P_{n-1} = P_n$. Suppose that $\#(P_1) \ge 2$. By (a), $\#(P_i) \le \#(P_{i+1})$ for every i. Since each equivalence class contains at least one state and $\#(K) = n$, $\#(P_i) \le n$ for all i. Thus either $\#(P_{n-1}) = n$, in which case $P_{n-1} = P_n$, or else there exists an integer $k \le n - 1$ so that $\#(P_k) = \#(P_{k+1})$. If the latter occurs, then $P_k = P_{k+1}$, since P_{k+1} is a refinement of P_k [by (a)]. In either case, $P_{n-1} = P_n$.

	I^1		I^2	
q_1	q_3	0	q_5	0
q_2	q_4	0	q_6	0
q_3	q_3	0	q_5	1
q_4	q_4	0	q_6	1
q_5	q_5	0	q_1	0
q_6	q_6	0	q_2	0

FIGURE 1.12

	I^1		I^2	
q_1	q_2	1	q_1	1
q_2	q_1	1	q_2	1
q_3	q_4	1	q_4	1
q_4	q_5	1	q_5	1
q_5	q_6	1	q_6	1
q_6	q_7	1	q_7	1
q_7	q_3	1	q_3	2

FIGURE 1.13

	I^1	
q_1	q_2	0
q_2	q_3	0
q_3	q_4	1
q_4	q_5	0
q_5	q_6	0
q_6	q_1	0

FIGURE 1.14

EXAMPLE 3. Let S be the machine in Fig. 1.12. Then

$$\overset{1}{\equiv} = Q \cup \{(q_1, q_2), (q_1, q_5), (q_1, q_6), (q_2, q_5), (q_2, q_6), (q_3, q_4), (q_5, q_6)\},$$

$$\text{where } Q = \{(q_i, q_i) | 1 \leq i \leq 6\};$$

$$\overset{2}{\equiv} = Q \cup \{(q_1, q_2), (q_3, q_4), (q_5, q_6)\};$$

and

$$\overset{3}{\equiv} = \overset{2}{\equiv}.$$

By (c) of Lemma 1.2, the set of pairs (p, q) for which $p \equiv q$ is $\overset{2}{\equiv}$.

EXERCISE 2. Find the set of pairs of equivalent states in the machine in (a) Fig. 1.13, (b) Fig. 1.14. Also, determine the equivalence classes generated by $\equiv$.

	I^1	
q_1	q_2	0
q_2	q_3	0
$\vdots$		
q_{n-1}	q_n	0
q_n	q_1	1

FIGURE 1.15

Theorem 1.1. Let S be a sequential machine with n states. States p and q in S are equivalent if and only if $\lambda(p, J) = \lambda(q, J)$ for every tape J of length $n - 1$, that is, if and only if $p \overset{n-1}{\equiv} q$. Furthermore, the number $n - 1$ is the smallest possible in the general case.

Proof. Obviously it may be assumed that $n \geq 2$. By (e) of Lemma 1.2, $P_{n-1} = P_n$. By (c) of Lemma 1.2, p and q are equivalent if and only if $p \overset{n-1}{\equiv} q$.

To see that the number $n - 1$ cannot be reduced, let S be the machine (called a *mod n counter*) in Fig. 1.15. For each positive integer k there is only one tape J_k of length k. The states q_1 and q_2 are not equivalent since $\lambda(q_1, J_{n-1}) = (0)^{n-1}$ and $\lambda(q_2, J_{n-1}) = (0)^{n-2}1$. For $k < n - 1$, however, we have

$$\lambda(q_1, J_k) = \lambda(q_2, J_k) = (0)^k.$$

Theorem 1.1 derives the best bound on the length of tapes necessary for determining whether particular states in the *same* machine are equivalent. The best bound for the case when the states are in *different* machines is now derived.

Theorem 1.2. Let S and T be sequential machines with n_1 and n_2 states, respectively. Let $\Sigma_S = \Sigma_T$. Then states p in S and q in T are equivalent if and only if $\lambda_S(p, J) = \lambda_T(q, J)$ for every tape J of length $n_1 + n_2 - 1$. Furthermore, the number $n_1 + n_2 - 1$ is the smallest possible in the general case.

Proof. Without loss of generality it may be assumed that the symbols for the states in S are distinct from the symbols for the states in T. Let U be the machine which is the "direct sum" of S and T, that is, the machine whose δ, λ matrix consists of the δ, λ matrix of T placed directly under that

	I^1		I^2	
p_1	p_2	1	p_2	1
p_2	p_3	0	p_1	0
$\vdots$				
p_{n-1}	p_n	0	p_{n-2}	0
p_n	p_n	0	p_{n-1}	0

FIGURE 1.16

	I^1		I^2	
q_1	q_2	1	q_2	1
q_2	q_3	0	q_1	0
$\vdots$				
q_{n-1}	q_n	0	q_{n-2}	0
q_n	q_{n-1}	0	q_n	0

FIGURE 1.17(a) $(n \geq 3)$

	I^1		I^2	
q_1	q_2	1	q_2	1
q_2	q_2	0	q_2	0

FIGURE 1.17(b) $(n = 2)$

of S. The resulting δ, λ matrix has $n_1 + n_2$ distinct rows due to the assumption on the symbols of the states in S and T. Thus U has $n_1 + n_2$ states. Let p be a state in S and q in T. Clearly p considered in S is equivalent to p considered in U, and q in T is equivalent to q in U. By Theorem 1.1, states p and q, considered in U, are equivalent if $p \overset{n_1 + n_2 - 1}{\equiv} q$. Thus p in S and q in T are equivalent if $\lambda_S(p, J) = \lambda_T(q, J)$ for every tape J of length $n_1 + n_2 - 1$.

To see that the number $n_1 + n_2 - 1$ cannot be reduced, we must consider two cases.*

(a) Suppose that $n_1 = n_2 = n$. If $n = 1$, then $n_1 + n_2 - 1 = 1$ obviously cannot be reduced. Assume $n \geq 2$. Let S and T be the machines in Figs. 1.16 and 1.17, respectively. Consider the states p_1 and q_1. Let $J_0 = (I^1)^{n-1}(I^2)^n$. Then $\lambda_S(p_1, J_0) \neq \lambda_T(q_1, J_0)$. However, as is easily seen, $\lambda_S(p_1, J) = \lambda_T(q_1, J)$ for any tape J of length $< n + n - 1$.

---

* An example is given in [G1] which does not require consideration of two cases.

	I^1		I^2	
p_1	p_2	1	p_2	1
p_2	p_3	0	p_1	0
p_3	p_4	0	p_2	0
$\vdots$				
p_{n_2}	p_{n_2+1}	0	p_{n_2-1}	0
p_{n_2+1}	p_{n_2+2}	0	p_{n_2-1}	0
$\vdots$				
p_{n_1-1}	p_{n_1}	0	p_{n_2-1}	0
p_{n_1}	p_{n_1}	0	p_{n_1}	0

FIGURE 1.18

	I^1		I^2	
q_1	q_2	1	q_2	1
q_2	q_3	0	q_1	0
q_3	q_4	0	q_2	0
$\vdots$				
q_{n_2-1}	q_{n_2}	0	q_{n_2-2}	0
q_{n_2}	q_{n_2}	0	q_{n_2-1}	0

FIGURE 1.19

	I^1	
p_1	p_2	0
p_2	p_1	0
p_3	p_2	1

FIGURE 1.20

	I^1	
q_1	q_2	2
q_2	q_2	0

FIGURE 1.21

	I^1	
p_1	p_2	0
p_2	p_1	0
p_3	p_2	1
q_1	q_2	2
q_2	q_2	0

FIGURE 1.22

	I^1	
p_1	p_1	0
p_2	p_1	1
p_3	p_3	1
p_4	p_3	1

FIGURE 1.23

	I^1	
q_1	q_2	0
q_2	q_2	0
q_3	q_1	1
q_4	q_4	1

FIGURE 1.24

(b) Suppose that $n_1 > n_2$. Consider the machines S and T in Figs. 1.18 and 1.19, respectively. Let $J_0 = (I^1)^{n_1-1}(I^2)^{n_2}$. Then $\lambda_S(p_1, J_0) \neq \lambda_T(q_1, J_0)$. However, as is easily seen, $\lambda_S(p_1, J) = \lambda_T(q_1, J)$ for every tape J of length $< n_1 + n_2 - 1$.

The proof of Theorem 1.2 indicates a procedure for finding all pairs (p, q) of states p in S and q in T for which $p \equiv q$. This consists of forming the direct sum of S and T, applying (c) of Lemma 1.2, and then removing those pairs of states which are in just one of the machines.

EXAMPLE 4. Let S and T be the machines in Figs. 1.20 and 1.21, respectively. The machine U which is the direct sum of S and T is in Fig. 1.22. A calculation of the $\overset{k}{\equiv}$ yields

$$\overset{1}{\equiv} = Q \cup \{(p_1, p_2), (p_1, q_2), (p_2, q_2)\},$$

$$\text{where } Q = \{(x, x)| x \text{ in } K_S \cup K_T\};$$

and

$$\overset{2}{\equiv} = \overset{1}{\equiv}.$$

The set of those pairs (p, q) of equivalent states p in S and q in T is $\{(p_1, q_2), (p_2, q_2)\}$.

EXERCISE 3. Let S and T be the machines in Figs. 1.23 and 1.24, respectively. Find the set of those pairs (p, q) of equivalent states p in S and q in T.

We now turn to the problem of constructing for an arbitrary machine S, a machine which is equivalent to S and which has the fewest number of states possible. Besides being of mathematical interest, this problem is of importance in the application of machines to the design of sequential switching circuits (Section 1.3). First, though, we need a preliminary result.

Lemma 1.3. Let S and T be sequential machines, with $\Sigma_S = \Sigma_T$. Let * be a relation between K_S and K_T which satisfies the following properties:

(1) If $p * q$ holds, then $\lambda_S(p, I) = \lambda_T(q, I)$ for each I in Σ.

(2) If $p * q$ holds, then $\delta_S(p, I) * \delta_T(q, I)$ holds for each I in Σ.

(3) For each state p there is at least one state q, and for each q at least one p, such that $p * q$ holds.

Then (i) $p \equiv q$ if $p * q$ holds, and (ii) $S \equiv T$.

	I^1	I^2
q_1	q_2 1	q_1 0
q_2	q_1 0	q_2 1
q_3	q_3 1	q_1 1

	I^1	I^2
p_1	p_2 1	p_1 0
p_2	p_1 0	p_2 1
p_3	p_3 1	p_1 1

FIGURE 1.25   FIGURE 1.26

Proof. Assume that $\lambda_S(x, J) = \lambda_T(y, J)$ for all tapes J of length $i \le k$ and all pairs (x, y) of states for which $x * y$ holds. By (1), this is true for $k = 1$. Let $I_1 \ldots I_{k+1}$ be any tape of length $k + 1$. Then $I_2 \ldots I_{k+1}$ is of length k. Let p and q be any states for which $p * q$ holds. By (2), $\delta_S(p, I_1) * \delta_T(q, I_1)$ holds. By (1), $\lambda_S(p, I_1) = \lambda_T(q, I_1)$. By the induction hypothesis

$$\lambda_S[\delta_S(p, I_1), I_2 \ldots I_{k+1}] = \lambda_T[\delta_T(q, I_1), I_2 \ldots I_{k+1}].$$

Then

$$\lambda_S(p, I_1 \ldots I_{k+1}) = \lambda_S(p, I_1)\lambda_S[\delta_S(p, I_1), I_2 \ldots I_{k+1}]$$
$$= \lambda_T(q, I_1)\lambda_T[\delta_T(q, I_1), I_2 \ldots I_{k+1}]$$
$$= \lambda_T(q, I_1 \ldots I_{k+1}).$$

Thus the induction is extended. Hence (i) is true.

From (3), for each state p there is at least one state q and for each q at least one p so that $p * q$, thus $p \equiv q$, holds. Therefore $S \equiv T$ and the lemma is proved.

Definition 1.5. Let S and T be sequential machines with $\Sigma_S = \Sigma_T$. Then S is said to be *isomorphic* to T if there exists a one-to-one mapping f of K_S *onto* K_T such that $\lambda_S(q, I) = \lambda_T[f(q), I]$ and $f[\delta_S(q, I)] = \delta_T[f(q), I]$ for all I in Σ_S and all states q in K_S.

Observe that machines are isomorphic if they have the same δ, λ matrix except for a relabeling of the states. A relabeling of either the inputs or the outputs is not permitted.

EXAMPLE 5. The machines in Figs. 1.25 and 1.26 are isomorphic under the mapping f which, for each i, takes q_i into p_i.

Unsolved problem. Let Σ and Δ be two nonempty sets. In terms of n, $\#(\Sigma)$, and $\#(\Delta)$, how many nonisomorphic machines S with n states are there for which $\Sigma_S = \Sigma$ and $\Delta_S = \Delta$?

Theorem 1.3. Among all machines equivalent to a given sequential machine S there is a unique (up to an isomorphism) one which has the fewest number of states. In other words, there is a unique "minimal-state" sequential machine equivalent to S. Furthermore, this machine is distinguished, that is, contains no two equivalent states.

Proof. Define a machine T as follows. $\Sigma_T = \Sigma_S$ and $\Delta_T = \Delta_S$. The states of T are the different equivalence classes $[q]$ of S generated by $\equiv$. Let A be an equivalence class and I an element of Σ_T. Let q be any element of A. Define $\lambda_T(A, I)$ to be $\lambda_S(q, I)$ and $\delta_T(A, I)$ to be $[\delta_S(q, I)]$. Suppose that p is another element in A (if there is one). By definition of A, $p \equiv q$. By Lemma 1.1, $\delta_S(p, I) \equiv \delta_S(q, I)$. Hence $[\delta_S(p, I)] = [\delta_S(q, I)]$. As $p \equiv q$, $\lambda_S(p, I) = \lambda_S(q, I)$. Thus the definitions of δ_T and λ_T are independent of the particular state q selected in A. Hence T is a machine.

We now show that S and T are equivalent machines. Let $*$ be the relation between K_S and K_T defined by $q * A$ holding if and only if q is in A. Clearly conditions (1) and (3) in Lemma 1.3 are satisfied. Condition (2) follows from the definition of δ_T. Then $*$ satisfies the hypotheses of Lemma 1.3. Thus $q \equiv [q]$ for each state q, and $S \equiv T$.

Next let W be any machine equivalent to S. To each state x in W there corresponds a state $p(x)$ in S equivalent to x. As $p(x) \equiv [p(x)]$, by the transitivity of $\equiv$, $x \equiv [p(x)]$. Let p' be any state in S for which $x \equiv p'$. Then $p' \equiv p(x)$, whence $[p'] = [p(x)]$. Thus, given x in W, the state $[p(x)]$ in T is uniquely determined. On the other hand, suppose that A is a state in T. There exists an element q in A. Then $q \equiv A$. As $S \equiv W$, there is a state y in W, so that $y \equiv q$. Then $y \equiv A$. Thus the association f of x into $[p(x)]$ is uniquely determined; that is, f is a mapping of K_W onto K_T. Therefore $\#(K_T) \leq \#(K_W)$. Hence T is equivalent to S and has the fewest states possible.

Suppose that T contains two equivalent states. The equivalence classes generated by $\equiv$ in T yield a machine T', $T' \equiv T \equiv S$, with fewer states than T. Since this contradicts the minimality property of T, it follows that T is distinguished.

Finally, suppose that W is a machine equivalent to S such that $\#(K_W) = \#(K_T)$. Then the mapping f, which takes x in W into $[p(x)]$ in T, is one-to-one. Furthermore, $\lambda_W(x, I) = \lambda_T([p(x)], I)$ for each I in Σ_T. By Lemma 1.1, $\delta_W(x, I) \equiv \delta_T([p(x)], I)$, since $x \equiv [p(x)]$. Since $\delta_T([p(x)], I) \equiv f(\delta_W(x, I))$ and T is distinguished, $\delta_T([p(x)], I) = f(\delta_W(x, I))$; that is, $\delta_T(f(x), I) = f(\delta_W(x, I))$ for each state x in W and each input I. Thus T and W are isomorphic; that is, there is just one minimal-state machine equivalent to S (up to isomorphism). (Q.E.D.)

It is now easy to obtain the smallest-state machine equivalent to a given machine S. Using (c) of Lemma 1.2, first derive the set of equiva-

	I^1	I^2
q_1	q_1 1	q_1 0
q_2	q_2 1	q_1 0
q_3	q_5 0	q_3 1
q_4	q_3 1	q_4 0
q_5	q_3 0	q_5 1

FIGURE 1.27

	I^1	I^2
p_1	p_1 1	p_1 0
p_2	p_3 1	p_2 0
p_3	p_3 0	p_3 1

FIGURE 1.28

lence classes generated by $\equiv$ between states of S. Then construct a machine from these equivalence classes by the method described in Theorem 1.3. This procedure is frequently called the "merging technique" [H2].

EXAMPLE 6. Let S be the machine in Fig. 1.27. Calculation of the $\overset{k}{\equiv}$ yields

$$\overset{1}{\equiv} = \{(q_1, q_2), (q_1, q_4), (q_2, q_4), (q_3, q_5)\} \cup Q,$$

$$\text{where } Q = \{(q_i, q_i) | 1 \leq i \leq 5\};$$

$$\overset{2}{\equiv} = \{(q_1, q_2), (q_3, q_5)\} \cup Q;$$

and

$$\overset{3}{\equiv} = \overset{2}{\equiv} = \equiv.$$

Then $P_2 = P_3 = \{\langle q_1, q_2 \rangle, \langle q_3, q_5 \rangle, \langle q_4 \rangle\}$. Define the states of the minimal-state machine T equivalent to S to be the different equivalence classes; that is,

$$p_1 = \langle q_1, q_2 \rangle, \quad p_2 = \langle q_4 \rangle, \quad \text{and} \quad p_3 = \langle q_3, q_5 \rangle.$$

When T is constructed by the method in Theorem 1.3, its δ, λ matrix is in Fig. 1.28.

EXERCISE 4. Find the minimal-state machine equivalent to the machine in (a) Fig. 1.29, (b) Fig. 1.30.

EXERCISE 5. *A generalized sequential machine* is a 5-tuple $(K, \Sigma, \Delta, \delta, \lambda)$, where K, Σ, Δ, and δ are the same as in the definition of a sequential machine, and λ associates with each pair (q, I) in $K \times \Sigma$, a (possibly empty) finite sequence of elements of Δ. Extend δ and λ to all pairs (q, J), where q is a state and J is a tape, as in a sequential machine. Call an infinite sequence $\{x_n\}$ of elements *ultimately periodic* if there exists integers n_0 and n_1 such that $x_{n+n_1} = x_n$ for every integer $n \geq n_0$. Show

	I^1		I^2	
q_1	q_2	0	q_2	0
q_2	q_3	0	q_3	0
q_3	q_4	0	q_4	0
q_4	q_4	1	q_4	0
q_5	q_6	0	q_5	1
q_6	q_5	0	q_6	1

FIGURE 1.29

	I^1		I^2	
q_1	q_2	0	q_3	0
q_2	q_2	0	q_2	1
q_3	q_2	0	q_3	1
q_4	q_5	1	q_1	0
q_5	q_6	1	q_5	0
q_6	q_5	1	q_5	0
q_7	q_3	0	q_6	0

FIGURE 1.30

that in a generalized sequential machine, if $\{I_k\}$ is an ultimately periodic sequence of inputs, then the resulting sequence $\{E_k\}$ of outputs, denoted by $\lambda(q, \{I_k\}) = \{E_k\}$, is also ultimately periodic.

EXERCISE 6. Let N denote the non-negative integers. For each integer x in N let $f(x)$ denote the sequence of $x + 1$ consecutive 1's. For example, $f(3) = 1, 1, 1, 1$. For each finite sequence of symbols $E_1 \ldots E_k$, let $g(E_i \ldots E_k)$ be the number of 1's in $E_1 \ldots E_k$.* To each generalized sequential machine S, where Σ contains the symbol 1, and each start state q, consider the function S_q defined by $S_q(x) = g[\lambda(q, f(x))]$ for each x in N.†

(i) Show that S_q is an increasing function; i.e., if $x \leq y$, then

$$S_q(x) \leq S_q(y).$$

(ii) Show that the infinite sequence $\{y_n\}$, defined by $y_0 = S_q(0)$ and $y_n = S_q(n) - S_q(n - 1)$ for $n \geq 1$, is ultimately periodic.

(iii) Let h be an increasing function from N into N such that the sequence $\{y_n\}$, where $y_0 = h(0)$ and $y_n = h(n) - h(n - 1)$, is ultimately periodic. Prove that there exists a generalized sequential machine S and a state q such that $S_q = h$.

(iv) Prove that the result in (iii) is no longer true if S is required to be a sequential machine, even when h has the property that $h(n) < h(n + 1)$ for all n.

---

* See reference [D1].

† S_q is another manifestation of the work performed by S at q.

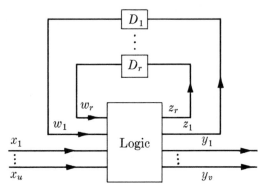

FIGURE 1.31

1.3 An application. * An important class of circuits which occurs in engineering is that of sequential switching circuits. A (synchronous) sequential switching circuit is a configuration of physical elements as pictured in Fig. 1.31. Time is considered as divided into discrete units. Here each x_i, y_j, z_k, and w_k is a wire which at each time t assumes one of the two values 0 or 1 (actually a "low" or a "high" voltage). Each D_k is a delay element (or storage bin) which at each time t contains either a 0 or a 1 (actually the delay element is in one of two stable configurations). Denote by x_i^t, y_j^t, z_k^t, w_k^t, and D_k^t the value of the appropriate wire or delay element at time t. Let

$$x^t = (x_1^t, \ldots, x_u^t), \qquad y^t = (y_1^t, \ldots, y_v^t),$$

$$w^t = (w_1^t, \ldots, w_r^t), \qquad z^t = (z_1^t, \ldots, z_r^t),$$

and

$$D^t = (D_1^t, \ldots, D_r^t).$$

We call x^t the input, D^t the state, and y^t the output of the circuit at time t. The physical devices in the box labeled "Logic" are called *logical elements*. They transform the variables $w_1, \ldots, w_r, x_1, \ldots, x_u$ into $v + r$ functions $y_i^t = f_i(w^t, x^t)$ and $z_k^t = g_k(w^t, x^t)$. How they do this is of no concern to us.

The circuit acts thus. At time t the input x^t is supplied by an external source and enters the logic box. Simultaneously, each w_k^t assumes the value D_k^t, that is, $w^t = D^t$, and w^t then enters the logic box. The logical elements then execute their transformations instantaneously, producing y^t and z^t. The output y^t goes to an external destination. For each k, z_k^t enters

---

* This section may be omitted on a first reading.

(x_1, x_2) D_1	(0,0)	(0,1)	(1,0)	(1,1)
0	0,0	1,0	1,0	0,0
1	1,1	0,0	1,0	1,0

FIGURE 1.32

	I^1	I^2	I^3	I^4
q_1	q_1 0	q_2 0	q_2 0	q_1 0
q_2	q_2 1	q_1 0	q_2 0	q_2 0

FIGURE 1.33

D_k in such a manner that $D_k^{t+1} = z_k^t$. The equations describing the circuit thus have the form

$$D_k^{t+1} = w_k^{t+1} = g_k(D^t, x^t)$$

and

$$y_i^t = f_i(D^t, x^t)$$

for $1 \le k \le r$ and $1 \le i \le v$. The sequential switching circuit acts as a sequential machine, with the next state function determined by the equations $D_k^{t+1} = g_k(D^t, x^t)$, and the output function by the equations $y_i^t = f_i(D^t, x^t)$.

EXAMPLE 1. Consider the sequential switching circuit whose equations are

$$D_1^{t+1} = g_1(D_1^t, x_1^t, x_2^t)$$

and

$$y_1^t = f_1(D_1^t, x_1^t, x_2^t),$$

where $g_1(0, 0, 0) = g_1(1, 0, 1) = g_1(0, 1, 1) = 0$, $g_1 = 1$ otherwise, $f_1(1, 0, 0) = 1$, and $f_1 = 0$ otherwise. There are four inputs ($x_1 = 0, 1$; $x_2 = 0, 1$), namely, (0, 0), (0, 1), (1, 0), and (1, 1). There are two states, $D_1 = 0$ and $D_1 = 1$. The δ, λ matrix of the circuit, considered as a sequential machine, is shown in Fig. 1.32. It is rewritten in more familiar form in Fig. 1.33, where $I^1 = (0, 0)$, $I^2 = (0, 1)$, $I^3 = (1, 0)$, $I^4 = (1, 1)$, q_1 represents $D_1 = 0$, and q_2 represents $D_1 = 1$.

EXERCISE 1. Write a δ, λ matrix associated with each of the following circuit equations:

(i)
$$D_1^{t+1} = g_1(D_1^t, x_1^t, x_2^t),$$
$$y_1^{t+1} = f_1(D_1^t, x_1^t, x_2^t),$$

and

$$y_2^{t+1} = f_2(D_1^t, x_1^t, x_2^t),$$

where

$$g_1(1, 1, 0) = g_1(0, 1, 1) = 1,$$
$$g_1 = 0 \quad \text{otherwise},$$
$$f_1(0, 0, 0) = f_1(1, 0, 1) = f_1(1, 1, 0) = 1,$$
$$f_1 = 0 \quad \text{otherwise},$$

and

$$f_2(0, 0, 1) = f_2(0, 1, 0) = f_2(1, 0, 1) = 0,$$
$$f_2 = 1 \quad \text{otherwise}.$$

(ii)
$$D_1^{t+1} = g_1(D_1^t, D_2^t, x_1^t),$$
$$D_2^{t+1} = g_2(D_1^t, D_2^t, x_1^t),$$
$$y_1^t = f_1(D_1^t, D_2^t, x_1^t),$$

and

$$y_2^t = f_2(D_1^t, D_2^t, x_1^t),$$

where

$$g_1(0, 0, 0) = g_1(1, 1, 1) = 0,$$
$$g_1 = 1 \quad \text{otherwise},$$
$$g_2(1, 0, 0) = g_2(1, 0, 1) = g_2(0, 1, 0) = 0,$$
$$g_2 = 1 \quad \text{otherwise},$$
$$f_1(0, 0, 1) = 0,$$
$$f_1 = 1 \quad \text{otherwise},$$

and

$$f_2(1, 0, 1) = f_2(0, 1, 1) = f_2(1, 0, 0) = 1,$$
$$f_2 = 0 \quad \text{otherwise}.$$

A sequential switching circuit may be regarded as a sequential machine. The converse is also true; that is, each sequential machine may be repre-

	I^1	I^2	I^3
q_1	$q_2 \quad E^1$	$q_1 \quad E^2$	$q_2 \quad E^2$
q_2	$q_1 \quad E^1$	$q_3 \quad E^2$	$q_1 \quad E^1$
q_3	$q_2 \quad E^2$	$q_3 \quad E^1$	$q_1 \quad E^2$

FIGURE 1.34

(x_1, x_2) / (D_1, D_2)	(0,0)	(0,1)	(1,1)
(0,0)	(0,1),0	(0,0),1	(0,1),1
(0,1)	(0,0),0	(1,0),1	(0,0),0
(1,0)	(0,1),1	(1,0),0	(0,0),1

FIGURE 1.35

sented by at least one sequential switching circuit.* This statement depends on the fact that any system of equations

$$y_i^t = f_i(w^t, x^t), \qquad i = 1, \ldots, v$$

may be realized by suitable connections of logical elements, i.e., by a logic box. A proof of this fact, together with additional details on logical elements and sequential switching circuits, is found in [C1].

EXAMPLE 2. Consider the machine S in Fig. 1.34. In realizing this machine by some sequential switching circuit, it is sufficient to find an appropriate system of circuit equations. Since S has three states, at least two delay elements D_1 and D_2 are needed. Let $(D_1 = 0, D_2 = 0)$, $(D_1 = 0, D_2 = 1)$, and $(D_1 = 1, D_2 = 0)$ represent q_1, q_2, and q_3, respectively. Similarly two wires x_1 and x_2 are needed to "code" the three inputs, and one output wire y_1 is needed for the outputs. Let $(x_1 = 0, x_2 = 0)$, $(x_1 = 0, x_2 = 1)$, and $(x_1 = 1, x_2 = 1)$ represent I^1, I^2, and I^3, respectively. Let $y_1 = 0$ represent E^1 and $y_1 = 1$ represent E^2. Replacing each state, each input, and each output in Fig. 1.34 by its appropriate code, we derive Fig. 1.35. The circuit equations are now

---

* Here it is understood that one is allowed to change the names of the inputs, states, and outputs, that is, "code" the inputs, states, and outputs in terms of 0, 1 sequences.

	I^1		I^2	
q_1	q_2	0	q_4	1
q_2	q_3	1	q_1	2
q_3	q_1	0	q_2	2
q_4	q_3	2	q_2	1

FIGURE 1.36

	I^1		I^2		I^3	
q_1	q_2	E^0	q_5	E^1	q_1	E^0
q_2	q_4	E^1	q_3	E^0	q_2	E^1
q_3	q_1	E^2	q_4	E^1	q_5	E^2
q_4	q_1	E^2	q_1	E^0	q_2	E^1
q_5	q_4	E^1	q_3	E^2	q_1	E^0

FIGURE 1.37

derived from Fig. 1.35. These are

$$D_1^{t+1} = g_1(D_1^t, D_2^t, x_1^t, x_2^t), \qquad D_2^{t+1} = g_2(D_1^t, D_2^t, x_1^t, x_2^t),$$

and

$$y_1^t = f_1(D_1^t, D_2^t, x_1^t, x_2^t),$$

where

$$g_1(0, 1, 0, 1) = g_1(1, 0, 0, 1) = 1,$$
$$g_1 = 0 \quad \text{otherwise,}$$
$$g_2(0, 0, 0, 0) = g_2(1, 0, 0, 0) = g_2(0, 0, 1, 1) = 1,$$
$$g_2 = 0 \quad \text{otherwise,}$$

and

$$f_1(0, 0, 0, 0) = f_1(0, 1, 0, 0) = f_1(1, 0, 0, 1)$$
$$= f_1(0, 1, 1, 1) = 0,$$
$$f_1 = 1 \quad \text{otherwise.}$$

EXERCISE 2. Find a sequential switching circuit which realizes the machine in (a) Fig. 1.36, (b) Fig. 1.37.

The minimization technique of Theorem 1.3 enables us to reduce the number of states in a given machine whenever possible. Suppose that this procedure is applied to the sequential machine S associated with a sequential switching circuit C. Let T be the resulting machine. Suppose we use the same input code and output code respectively for T which we used in going from C to S. Then we obtain a sequential switching circuit C' with the same input versus output behavior as C and with possibly fewer delay elements.

x_1 (D_1, D_2)	0	1
(0,0)	(0,1),1	(0,0),1
(0,1)	(0,1),1	(0,0),0
(1,0)	(1,1),1	(1,0),1
(1,1)	(1,1),1	(1,0),0

FIGURE 1.38

	0	1
q_1	q_2 1	q_1 1
q_2	q_2 1	q_1 0
q_3	q_4 1	q_3 1
q_4	q_4 1	q_3 0

FIGURE 1.39

	0	1
p_1	p_2 1	p_1 1
p_2	p_2 1	p_1 0

FIGURE 1.40

x_1 D_3	0	1
0	1,1	0,1
1	1,1	0,0

FIGURE 1.41

EXAMPLE 3. Consider the sequential switching circuit whose circuit equations are

$$D_1^{t+1} = g_1(D_1^t, D_2^t, x_1^t),$$
$$D_2^{t+1} = g_2(D_1^t, D_2^t, x_1^t),$$

and

$$y_1^t = f_1(D_1^t, D_2^t, x_1^t),$$

where

$$g_1(1, D_2^t, x_1^t) = 1, \qquad g_1 = 0 \quad \text{otherwise},$$
$$g_2(D_1^t, D_2^t, 0) = 1, \qquad g_2 = 0 \quad \text{otherwise},$$

and

$$f_1(0, 1, 1) = f_1(1, 1, 1) = 0, \qquad f_1 = 1 \quad \text{otherwise}.$$

The δ, λ matrix is shown in Fig. 1.38, and appears in a more familiar form in Fig. 1.39. By the technique of Theorem 1.3, the machine in Fig. 1.39 is reduced to the machine in Fig. 1.40. A coding for the states of the machine in Fig. 1.40 is given in Fig. 1.41 and involves just one delay element. The equations of the resulting sequential switching circuit are

$$D_3^{t+1} = g_3(D_3^t, x_1^t) \quad \text{and} \quad y_1^t = h_1(D_3^t, x_1^t),$$

where

$$g_3(D_3^t, 0) = 1,$$

$$g_3(D_3^t, 1) = 0,$$

and

$$h_1(1, 1) = 0,$$

$$h_1 = 1 \quad \text{otherwise.}$$

EXERCISE 3. Let C be the sequential switching circuit with two delay elements, one input wire, and one output wire, where

$$g_1(1, 0, 0) = g_1(0, 0, 1) = 1,$$

$$g_1 = 0 \quad \text{otherwise,}$$

$$g_2(0, 1, 1) = 1,$$

$$g_2 = 0 \quad \text{otherwise,}$$

and

$$f_1(0, 0, 0) = f_1(1, 0, 0) = 1,$$

$$f_1 = 0 \quad \text{otherwise.}$$

Does there exist a circuit whose behavior is the same as C and has fewer delay elements? If so, find one.

1.4 Strongly connected machines. Many physical machines, such as desk calculators, typewriters, and, of course, data processors, are able to pass from any state to any other by a sequence of intermediate states. We now briefly examine this property.

Definition 1.6. A sequential machine S is said to be *strongly connected* if for every ordered pair (p, q) of states in S there exists a tape J such that $\delta(p, J) = q$.

The machine given in Fig. 1.42 is strongly connected. The machine in Fig. 1.43 is not strongly connected, since there is no tape which takes q_2 to q_1.

Let S and T be machines, with S strongly connected. The next result asserts that if p is a state in S with the property that each input sequence versus output sequence at p is duplicated at some state q in T (q depending on the input sequence), then there is a state in T which duplicates *all* the input sequences versus output sequences at p.

	I^1	I^2
q_1	q_2 0	q_1 0
q_2	q_3 1	q_4 1
q_3	q_2 0	q_3 1
q_4	q_1 0	q_4 1

	I^1	I^2	I^3
q_1	q_1 0	q_2 1	q_2 0
q_2	q_3 0	q_2 0	q_3 1
q_3	q_3 0	q_2 1	q_3 0

FIGURE 1.42   FIGURE 1.43

Theorem 1.4. Let S and T be sequential machines having a common set of inputs, with S strongly connected. Let p be a state in S such that for each tape J there is a state q_J in T satisfying $\lambda_S(p, J) = \lambda_T(q_J, J)$. Then there is a state q in T which is equivalent to p.

Proof. Consider the following property:

(*)   There are states $\overline{p}$ in S and $\overline{q}$ in T such that $\overline{p} \equiv \overline{q}$.

If (*) holds, then, since S is strongly connected, there is a tape J such that $\delta(\overline{p}, J) = p$. This, by Lemma 1.1, implies that $p = \delta(\overline{p}, J) \equiv \delta(\overline{q}, J)$, whence the theorem is derived.

We now show that (*) is true. Assume that (*) is false. Denote by $q_1, \ldots, q_n$ the states of T. Since (*) is false, $p \not\equiv q_1$. Then there is a tape J_1 such that $\lambda(p, J_1) \neq \lambda(q_1, J_1)$. For $1 \leq k < n$ and each $i \leq k$ suppose that J_i is a tape for which $\lambda(p, J_1 \ldots J_i) \neq \lambda(q_i, J_1 \ldots J_i)$. Let $\overline{q}_k = \delta(q_{k+1}, J_1 \ldots J_k)$. Since (*) is false,

$$p_k = \delta(p, J_1 \ldots J_k) \not\equiv \overline{q}_k.$$

Hence there exists a tape J_{k+1} such that

$$\lambda(p_k, J_{k+1}) \neq \lambda(\overline{q}_k, J_{k+1}).$$

Then

$$\lambda(p, J_1 \ldots J_{k+1}) = \lambda(p, J_1 \ldots J_k)\lambda(p_k, J_{k+1})$$
$$\neq \lambda(q_{k+1}, J_1 \ldots J_k)\lambda(\overline{q}_k, J_{k+1})$$
$$= \lambda(q_{k+1}, J_1 \ldots J_{k+1}).$$

The induction is thus extended to $k + 1$, and therefore to all integers $k \leq n$. Then there is no state q such that $\lambda(p, J_1 \ldots J_n) = \lambda(q, J_1 \ldots J_n)$. Because $\lambda(p, J_1 \ldots J_i) \neq \lambda(q_i, J_1 \ldots J_i)$, it follows that $\lambda(p, J_1 \ldots J_n) \neq \lambda(q_i, J_1 \ldots J_n)$, for each i. This contradicts the hypothesis. Hence (*) holds and the theorem is proved.

	I^1	I^2
p_1	p_2 E^1	p_2 E^2
p_1	p_2 E^3	p_2 E^3

FIGURE 1.44

	I^1	I^2
q_1	q_3 E^1	q_3 E^1
q_2	q_3 E^2	q_3 E^2
q_3	q_3 E^3	q_3 E^3

FIGURE 1.45

Theorem 1.4 is no longer true if the hypothesis that S is strongly connected is removed. Consider the machines in Fig. 1.44 and 1.45, respectively. For each tape J beginning with I^1, $\lambda(q_1, J) = \lambda(p_1, J)$. For each tape J beginning with I^2, $\lambda(q_2, J) = \lambda(p_1, J)$. But there is no state q in the second machine which is equivalent to p_1.

EXERCISES. Prove each of the following.

1. Each machine S has a strongly connected submachine. (The machine T is said to be a *submachine* of S if $K_T \subseteq K_S$, $\Sigma_S = \Sigma_T$, δ_T is δ_S restricted to $K_T \times \Sigma_S$, and λ_T is λ_S restricted to $K_T \times \Sigma_S$.)

2. A machine S is strongly connected if and only if S has no submachine except itself.

3. Let S and T be distinguished strongly connected machines with some state p in S equivalent to some state q in T. Then S and T are isomorphic.

4. Let Z be a collection of machines with a common set of inputs Σ and outputs Δ, respectively. Suppose that (i) for each distinguished strongly connected machine $S = (K, \Sigma, \Delta, \delta, \lambda)$ there is a machine T in Z isomorphic to S, and (ii) each two machines in Z have no equivalent states. Then each machine in Z is strongly connected.

5. Let S have a state p with the property that to each state q in S there is a tape J for which $\delta(p, J) = q$. If S is not strongly connected then p is equivalent to no state in any strongly connected machine.

Unsolved problem. Let Σ and Δ be two nonempty finite sets. In terms of n, $\#(\Sigma)$, and $\#(\Delta)$, how many nonisomorphic strongly connected machines S with n states are there with $\Sigma_S = \Sigma$ and $\Delta_S = \Delta$?

1.5 Determination of terminal state. The problem now considered is that of starting a known sequential machine in an unknown initial state and, by subjecting the machine to a tape and observing the resultant output sequence, of determining the final state. In other words, suppose that A is a set of states of machine S and that the machine, initially, is in one of the states of A. A tape is inserted into the machine and the resulting output sequence observed. Based on this output sequence, another tape is inserted into the machine (which may no longer be at the original state). This procedure is continued until such time as one can deduce, from the total output sequence, the current state of the machine. The problem is to construct such a procedure.

If such a process is repeated for each state p in A, a set of tapes $\{J(p)|p$ in $A\}$ is obtained. Such a set is said to be an experiment.

Definition 1.7. Let S be a sequential machine and A a subset of K_S. For each element p in A, let $J(p)$ be a tape. If $J(p) = I_1 \ldots I_k$ and $1 \leq i \leq k$, denote by $J_i(p)$ the tape $I_1 \ldots I_i$. The set $\{J(p)|p$ in $A\}$ is said to be an *experiment* (for A) if the following three conditions hold for all states p and q:

   (i) $J_1(p) = J_1(q)$.

   (ii) If i is an integer less than the length of $J(p)$ such that $J_i(p) = J_i(q)$ and $\lambda(p, J_i(p)) = \lambda(q, J_i(q))$, then $J_{i+1}(p) = J_{i+1}(q)$.

   (iii) If $\lambda(p, J(p)) = \lambda(q, J(p))$, then $\delta(p, J(p)) = \delta(q, J(p))$.

Let us analyze the three axioms of an experiment. An experiment is the set of all the tapes which a procedure for determining the terminal state of a machine yields. Since, a priori, nothing is known about the unknown initial state in A, the first input in each $J(p)$ is the same [condition (i)]. Suppose the process has been in effect for several stages. Then the machine has been subjected to a tape M of length i. Based on the resulting output sequence, the unknown initial state is an element of a subset A_i of A. Thus $J_i(p) = M$ for each p in A_i. If another input I_{i+1} is inserted into the machine, then $MI_{i+1} = J_{i+1}(p)$ for every p in A_i [condition (ii)]. Suppose the process produces a tape M which is in the experiment. Let L be the output sequence due to the tape M. Let $A_M = \{p|\lambda(p, M) = L, p$ in $A\}$. Then condition (iii) demands that $\{\delta(p, M)|p$ in $A_M\}$ consist of one state, namely the current one. Conditions (ii) and (iii) together imply that $M = J(p)$ for each state p in A_M.

Definition 1.8. If $J(p) = J(q)$ for all states p and q in A, the experiment is said to be *uniform*. In other words, an experiment is uniform if it contains just one tape.

EXAMPLE 1. Let S be the machine given in Fig. 1.46 and let

$$A = \{q_1, q_2, q_3, q_4\}.$$

The set of tapes $\{J(q_i)|1 \leq i \leq 4\}$, where

$$J(q_1) = J(q_2) = I^1I^3 \quad \text{and} \quad J(q_3) = J(q_4) = I^1I^2,$$

is an experiment. Then

$$\lambda(q_1, J(q_1)) = 00,$$

$$\delta(q_1, J(q_1)) = q_4,$$

$$\lambda(q_2, J(q_2)) = 01,$$

$$\delta(q_2, J(q_2)) = q_3,$$

$$\lambda(q_3, J(q_3)) = 10,$$

$$\delta(q_3, J(q_3)) = q_2,$$

$$\lambda(q_4, J(q_4)) = 11,$$

and

$$\delta(q_4, J(q_4)) = q_1.$$

Suppose that S is in some unknown initial state. The first input to be inserted is I^1. Suppose the first output is 0. Then the second input is I^3 and the terminal state is q_4 or q_3, depending on whether the second output is 0 or 1. Suppose the first output is 1. Then the second input is I^2 and the terminal state is q_2 or q_1, depending on whether the second output is 0 or 1. For this particular machine the unknown initial state may be determined, but for many machines this is not possible.

EXERCISE 1. Let S be the machine given in Fig. 1.46. Let $A = \{q_1, q_2, q_3, q_4\}$.

(a) If $J(q_1) = J(q_2) = I^2I^1$ and $J(q_3) = J(q_4) = I^3I^3$, is $\{J(q_i)| 1 \le i \le 4\}$ an experiment?

(b) If $J(q_1) = J(q_2) = I^2I^2$ and $J(q_3) = J(q_4) = I^2I^3I^3$, is $\{J(q_i)| 1 \le i \le 4\}$ an experiment?

(c) If $J(q_1) = I^2I^2$, $J(q_2) = I^2$, and $J(q_3) = J(q_4) = I^2I^2I^3$, is $\{J(q_i)|1 \le i \le 4\}$ an experiment?

	I^1	I^2	I^3
q_1	q_3 0	q_2 0	q_1 0
q_2	q_4 0	q_1 1	q_2 0
q_3	q_1 1	q_3 0	q_4 0
q_4	q_2 1	q_4 0	q_3 1

FIGURE 1.46

	I^1	I^2
q_1	q_1 0	q_2 1
q_2	q_3 1	q_3 1
q_3	q_2 1	q_1 1

FIGURE 1.47

EXERCISE 2. Let S be the machine given in Fig. 1.47. Construct a uniform experiment for $A = \{q_1, q_2, q_3\}$.

Definition 1.9. The length of the longest tape in an experiment is called the *length of the experiment.*

We now consider this problem. "Given positive integers n and k, let $e(n, k)$ and $u(n, k)$ denote the smallest integers such that for each distinguished machine S with n states and each set A of k states there exists an experiment and uniform experiment for A of length $\leq e(n, k)$ and $\leq u(n, k)$, respectively. Calculate $e(n, k)$ and $u(n, k)$." In Theorem 1.5 we shall obtain the surprising result that $e(n, k) = u(n, k)$. First, though, we shall need four auxiliary lemmas.

Lemma 1.4. Let S be a distinguished sequential machine with n states. Then for each k, $1 \leq k < n$, P_k contains at least $k + 1$ classes.

Proof. Without loss of generality, it may be assumed that $n \geq 2$. By Lemma 1.2 (d) and (c), $\#(P_1) \geq 2$. Let k be the smallest integer such that $P_k = P_{k+1}$. By Theorem 1.1, $k \leq n - 1$. From the minimality of k and Lemma 1.2 (a), $\#(P_i) < \#(P_{i+1})$ for $1 \leq i < k$. Hence $\#(P_i) \geq i + 1$ for $i \leq k$. By (c) of Lemma 1.2 and the fact that S is distinguished, $\#(P_k) = n$. Thus $\#(P_i) = n \geq i + 1$ for $k \leq i \leq n - 1$. Hence $\#(P_i) \geq i + 1$ for $1 \leq i \leq n - 1$.

Lemma 1.5. Let S be a distinguished sequential machine with n states. Let $\{A_i | 1 \leq i \leq r\}$ be a family of nonempty sets of states of S. Suppose that $\#(\bigcup_i A_i) = k$, where $k > r$. Then there exists a tape J, of length $\leq n - k + r$, and a set A_i with two states p and q such that $\lambda(p, J) \neq \lambda(q, J)$.

Proof. Since $k > r$, $\#(P_{n-k+r}) \geq n - k + r + 1$ by Lemma 1.4. Suppose that for each i, $1 \leq i \leq r$, there exists a class $C(i)$ of P_{n-k+r} such that $A_i \subseteq C(i)$. Then there are at most r classes $C(i)$. Since $\#(\bigcup_i A_i) = k$, $\#(K_S - \bigcup_i A_i) = n - k$. Thus there are at most $n - k$ classes of P_{n-k+r} which are not some $C(i)$. Consequently there are at most $n - k + r$ classes in P_{n-k+r}, contradicting Lemma 1.4. Hence there is some set A_i which is a subset of no class B in P_{n-k+r}. Then for some two states p and q in A_i, there exists a tape J, of length $\leq n - k + r$, such that $\lambda(p, J) \neq \lambda(q, J)$. (Q.E.D.)

In order to prove a key lemma (Lemma 1.7), some additional notation and a preliminary result are needed.

Notation. Let F be a family of nonempty sets. Define the relation $*$ between sets of F as follows. For sets A and B in F, $A * B$ holds if and only if, for some integer i, there exists a sequence $A = A_1, \ldots, A_i = B$ of sets in F such that $A_j \cap A_{j+1} \neq \emptyset$ for each j, $1 \leq j < i$. Let $H(F) = \{C(A)|A$ in $F, C(A) = \cup_{A*B} B\}$.

Observe that $H(F)$ is a partition of $\cup_{A \text{ in } F} A$.

EXAMPLE 2. Let $F = \{A_i|1 \leq i \leq 4\}$, where each set A_i of real numbers is defined by

$$A_1 = \{x|0 \leq x \leq 1\} \cup \{3\},$$
$$A_2 = \{0\} \cup \{x|9 \leq x \leq 10\},$$
$$A_3 = \{4\} \cup \{x|7 \leq x \leq 8\},$$
$$A_4 = \{x|\tfrac{15}{2} \leq x \leq \tfrac{17}{2}\} \cup \{11\},$$
$$A_5 = \{6\}.$$

Then $H(F) = \{C(A_1), C(A_3), C(A_5)\}$, where $C(A_1) = A_1 \cup A_2, C(A_3) = A_3 \cup A_4$, and $C(A_5) = A_5$.

Lemma 1.6. Let $F = \{B(e)|e$ in $R\}$, where R and each $B(e)$ are finite nonempty sets. Then

$$\sum_{e \text{ in } R} \#[B(e)] - \#\left[\bigcup_{e \text{ in } R} B(e)\right] \geq \#(R) - \#[H(F)].$$

Proof. Let C be any element in $H(F)$ and let $D = \{e|e$ in $R, B(e) \subseteq C\}$. Since the elements in $H(F)$ are pairwise disjoint, it suffices to show that

$$\sum_{e \text{ in } D} \#[B(e)] - \#(C) \geq \#(D) - 1.$$

There exists a sequence $e_1, \ldots, e_{\#(D)}$, of length $\#(D)$, such that $D = \{e_i|1 \leq i \leq \#(D)\}$, and such that $[\cup_{j=1}^i B(e_j)] \cap B(e_{i+1}) \neq \emptyset$ for each i. Using induction we now show that

$$(*) \quad \sum_{j=1}^i \#[B(e_j)] - \#\left[\bigcup_{j=1}^i B(e_j)\right] \geq i - 1$$

for each i. Clearly $(*)$ is true for $i = 1$. Suppose that $(*)$ is true for $i \leq h < \#(D)$. For any two sets A and B, $A \cap B \neq \emptyset$, it is always true that $\#(A) + \#(B) - \#(A \cup B) \geq 1$. Therefore,

$$\#\left[\bigcup_{j=1}^h B(e_j)\right] + \#[B(e_{h+1})] - \#\left[\bigcup_{j=1}^{h+1} B(e_j)\right] \geq 1.$$

By the induction hypothesis

$$\sum_{j=1}^{h} \#[B(e_j)] - \#\left[\bigcup_{j=1}^{h} B(e_j)\right] \geq h - 1.$$

Then

$$\sum_{j=1}^{h+1} \#[B(e_j)] - \#\left[\bigcup_{j=1}^{h+1} B(e_j)\right]$$

$$\geq \sum_{j=1}^{h+1} \#[B(e_j)] + 1 - \#\left[\bigcup_{j=1}^{h} B(e_j)\right] - \#[B(e_{h+1})]$$

$$\geq h - 1 + 1 = h.$$

Thus (*) is true for $h + 1$. By induction, (*) is true for $i \leq \#(D)$. Thus

$$\sum_{e \text{ in } D} \#[B(e)] - \#(C) \geq \#(D) - 1,$$

whence we obtain the result.

Lemma 1.7. Let S be a distinguished sequential machine with n states. Let $\{A_i | 1 \leq i \leq r\}$ be a family of $r \geq 1$ nonempty, pairwise disjoint sets of states of S. Let $\#(\cup_i A_i) = k > r$. Then there exists a tape J, of length $\leq \sum_{n-k+r}^{n-1} i$ with the following property: For all states p and q in the same set A_i, if $\lambda(p, J) = \lambda(q, J)$, then $\delta(p, J) = \delta(q, J)$.

Proof. The proof is established by induction on the number $k - r$. Suppose that $k - r = 1$. Since the sets A_i are nonempty and disjoint, all but one of them has just one element, and one of them has just two elements. Let p and q be the only two states in a common A_i. By Lemma 1.5, there exists a tape J, of length $\leq n - k + r = n - 1$, such that $\lambda(p, J) \neq \lambda(q, J)$. Since $k - r = 1$, then $\sum_{n-k+r}^{n-1} i = n - 1$. Therefore J satisfies the lemma.

Suppose that the lemma holds when $k - r < w$, $w > 1$. Continuing by induction, assume $k - r = w$. By Lemma 1.5 there exists a tape J, of length $\leq n - k + r$, such that at least one of the sets A_i, say A_s, contains two elements p_0 and q_0 for which $\lambda(p_0, J) \neq \lambda(q_0, J)$. Denote by R the set of pairs

$$R = \{(i, L) | 1 \leq i \leq r, \lambda(p, J) = L \text{ for some } p \text{ in } A_i\}.$$

The set R has at least $r + 1$ elements. This is because (i) for each i there is at least one output sequence L such that (i, L) is in R, and (ii) for at least one i there exist two output sequences L_1 and L_2 such that (i, L_1) and (i, L_2) are both in R.

For each (i, L) in R denote by $B(i, L)$ the set

$$B(i, L) = \{\delta(p, J)|p \text{ in } A_i, \lambda(p, J) = L\}.$$

Two alternatives arise:

(a) Suppose that for each (i, L) in R, $B(i, L)$ contains at most one element. Let p and q be two states in any A_i such that $\lambda(p, J) = \lambda(q, J) = L$. Then both $\delta(p, J)$ and $\delta(q, J)$ are in $B(i, L)$. As $B(i, L)$ has only one element, $\delta(p, J) = \delta(q, J)$. Since $k > r$, it follows that $n - k + r \leq \sum_{n-k+r}^{n-1} i$. Therefore J satisfies the lemma.

(b) Suppose that one of the $B(i, L)$ has more than one element. Let $F = \{B(i, L)|(i, L) \text{ in } R\}$. Let $t = \#[H(F)]$, H being the function defined prior to Lemma 1.6, and

$$m = \#\left[\bigcup_{C \text{ in } H(F)} C\right] = \#\left[\bigcup_{(i,L) \text{ in } R} B(i, L)\right].$$

Consider the family $H(F)$. The sets in $H(F)$ are nonempty and pairwise disjoint. Since one of the sets in F has more than one element, $m > t$. It is now shown that $m - t < k - r$. Clearly R and F satisfy the hypothesis of Lemma 1.6. By Lemma 1.6,

$$\sum_{(i,L) \text{ in } R} \#[B(i, L)] - m \geq \#(R) - t.$$

Since

$$\bigcup_{(i,L) \text{ in } R} B(i, L) = \left\{\delta(p, J)|p \text{ in } \bigcup_{i=1}^{r} A_i\right\},$$

it follows that

$$\sum_{(i,L) \text{ in } R} \#[B(i, L)] \leq k.$$

As noted above, $\#(R) = r' > r$. Thus $k - m > r - t$, whence $m - t < k - r$.

The family $H(F)$ of sets satisfies the hypotheses of the lemma, with $m - t < w$. By the induction hypothesis, there exists a tape M, of length $\leq \sum_{n-m+t}^{n-1} i$, such that for any two states p and q in the same set C in $H(F)$, if $\lambda(p, M) = \lambda(q, M)$, then $\delta(p, M) = \delta(q, M)$.

Consider the tape JM. Let p and q be any two states in the same set A_i for which $\lambda(p, JM) = \lambda(q, JM)$. Then $\lambda(p, J) = \lambda(q, J)$. Thus both $\delta(p, J)$ and $\delta(q, J)$ are in $B(i, \lambda(p, J))$. There exists some set C in $H(F)$

such that $B(i, \lambda(p, J)) \subseteq C$. Hence both $\delta(p, J)$ and $\delta(q, J)$ are in C. Since $\lambda[\delta(p, J), M] = \lambda[\delta(q, J), M]$, then $\delta[\delta(p, J), M] = \delta[\delta(q, J), M]$. Thus $\delta(p, JM) = \delta(q, JM)$. Consider the length of JM. The length of J is at most $n - k + r$. Hence the length of JM is at most $n - k + r + \sum_{n-m+t}^{n-1} i$. Since $m - t < k - r$, then $n - k + r < n - m + t$. Thus the length of JM is at most $\sum_{n-k+r}^{n-1} i$. Consequently JM satisfies the lemma.

In either (a) or (b), therefore, the induction is extended to $k - r = w$. Thus the lemma is true for every integer. (Q.E.D.)

Using Lemma 1.7, the main result of this section will now be proved.

Theorem 1.5. $e(n, k) = u(n, k) = (2n - k)(k - 1)/2$.

Proof. Since a uniform experiment is also an experiment it is clear that $e(n, k) \leq u(n, k)$. It is thus sufficient to prove that

$$u(n, k) \leq \frac{(2n - k)(k - 1)}{2} \quad \text{and} \quad \frac{(2n - k)(k - 1)}{2} \leq e(n, k).$$

To see the first inequality let S be a distinguished machine with n states and A a set of k states of S. By Lemma 1.7, with $r = 1$, there exists a tape J, of length $\leq \sum_{n-k+1}^{n-1} i = (2n - k)(k - 1)/2$, with the following property: For all states p and q in A, if $\lambda(p, J) = \lambda(q, J)$, then $\delta(p, J) = \delta(q, J)$. Thus $\{J\}$ is a uniform experiment for A, of length

$$\leq \frac{(2n - k)(k - 1)}{2}.$$

Hence

$$u(n, k) \leq \frac{(2n - k)(k - 1)}{2}.$$

To see the second inequality, let S be the machine defined as follows.

$$K_S = \{q_i | 1 \leq i \leq n\}, \qquad \Sigma = \{I^i | 1 \leq i \leq n - 1\},$$

and

$$\Delta = \{0, 1\}.$$

Let $\delta(q_i, I^{n-1}) = q_i$ for all i. For $1 \leq j \leq n$ and $i \leq j$ or $j + 2 < i$, let $\delta(q_i, I^j) = q_i$. For $1 \leq j \leq n - 2$, let $\delta(q_{j+1}, I^j) = q_{j+2}$ and $\delta(q_{j+2}, I^j) = q_{j+1}$. Let $\lambda(q_n, I^{n-1}) = 1$, and $\lambda(q_i, I^j) = 0$ otherwise.

Consider the set $A = \{q_i | i \leq k\}$. It will now be shown that for any tape J of length $< (2n - k)(k - 1)/2$, there exists a state p in A, $p \neq q_1$, such that $\lambda(p, J) = \lambda(q_1, J)$ and $\delta(p, J) \neq \delta(q_1, J)$. To see this first note the following.

(1) $\delta(q_i, J) \neq \delta(q_j, J)$ for all distinct states q_i and q_j and for any tape J.

Since each input permutes the states of S, (1) holds. Next, for any tape $J = I_1 \ldots I_w$ let J_0 be the empty sequence, $\delta(p, J_0) = p$ for each state p, and $J_r = I_1 \ldots I_r$ for $r \leq w$. Then the following is true.

(2) Let J be any tape $J = I_1 \ldots I_w$. Suppose that q_i is a state in S such that $\lambda(q_i, J) \neq \lambda(q_1, J)$. Then for each integer j, $i \leq j \leq n$, there exists an integer $m(i, j)$, $1 \leq m(i, j) \leq w$, such that $\delta(q_i, J_{m(i,j)-1}) = q_j$ and $I_{m(i,j)} = I^{j-1}$.

The reasoning is this. Since $\lambda(q_1, J)$ is a sequence of 0's and $\lambda(q_i, J) \neq \lambda(q_1, J)$, $\lambda(q_i, J)$ must contain a 1. But the machine cannot give an output of 1 unless it is in state q_n. To move to state q_n from state q_i the machine must pass through $q_{i+1}, \ldots, q_{n-1}$. In doing this the $m(i, j)$ are obtained.

Now let $J = I_1 \ldots I_w$ be a tape of length w such that $\lambda(p, J) \neq \lambda(q_1, J)$ for each state $p \neq q_1$ in A. For each pair (i, j), where $2 \leq i \leq k$ and $i \leq j \leq n$, let $m(i, j)$ be defined as in (2). Suppose that $m(i, j) = m(g, h) = t$. Then $I_t = I^{j-1}$ and $I_t = I^{h-1}$. Thus $h = j$. Also, $\delta(q_i, J_{t-1}) = q_j$ and $\delta(q_g, J_{t-1}) = q_h$. Then $q_i = q_g$ by (1). Consequently $i = g$. Thus, if $m(i, j) = m(g, h)$, then $(i, j) = (g, h)$. Therefore all the $m(i, j)$ are distinct. The number of different (i, j) is

$$\sum_{i=2}^{k} \sum_{j=i}^{n} 1 = \sum_{i=2}^{k} (n - i + 1) = \frac{(2n - k)(k - 1)}{2}.$$

Since $1 \leq m(i, j) \leq w$ and the $m(i, j)$ are all distinct, it follows that $(2n - k)(k - 1)/2 \leq w$.

Let $\{J(p) | p \text{ in } A\}$ be any experiment for A. For each tape J of length $< (2n - k)(k - 1)/2$, there exists at least one state p in A, $p \neq q_1$, such that $\lambda(p, J) = \lambda(q_1, J)$ and $\delta(p, J) \neq \delta(q_1, J)$. Thus $J \neq J(q_1)$ by (iii) of Definition 1.7. Therefore the length of $J(q_1)$ is at least

$$\frac{(2n - k)(k - 1)}{2}.$$

Hence

$$\frac{(2n - k)(k - 1)}{2} \leq e(n, k). \qquad \text{(Q.E.D.)}$$

Corollary. To each distinguished sequential machine S with n states there exists a uniform experiment for S of length at most $n(n - 1)/2$. Furthermore, for each n there is a sequential machine S with n states so that each experiment for S has length at least $n(n - 1)/2$.

For a machine S and a set A of states of S, let $e(S, A)$ and $u(S, A)$ denote the length of a smallest experiment and a smallest uniform ex-

In fact, letting the unknown initial state be x, we find that

if $\quad x = q_1, \quad$ then $\quad \lambda(x, J) = 01000001 \quad$ and $\quad \delta(x, J) = q_3$;

if $\quad x = q_2, \quad$ then $\quad \lambda(x, J) = 10000000 \quad$ and $\quad \delta(x, J) = q_5$;

if $\quad x = q_3, \quad$ then $\quad \lambda(x, J) = 00001000 \quad$ and $\quad \delta(x, J) = q_5$;

if $\quad x = q_4, \quad$ then $\quad \lambda(x, J) = 00000001 \quad$ and $\quad \delta(x, J) = q_3$;

if $\quad x = q_5, \quad$ then $\quad \lambda(x, J) = 00000000 \quad$ and $\quad \delta(x, J) = q_5$;

if $\quad x = q_6, \quad$ then $\quad \lambda(x, J) = 00000000 \quad$ and $\quad \delta(x, J) = q_5$.

Thus, by inserting the tape J into the machine at some unknown state and observing the output sequence, we can determine the state $\delta(x, J)$.

Note that we cannot always determine the unknown initial state since q_5 and q_6 both yield the same output sequence.

EXERCISE 3. Let S be the machine given in Fig. 1.49 and

$$A = \{q_1, q_3, q_4, q_5\}.$$

Find a uniform experiment for A of length ≤ 9.

EXERCISE 4. Let S be the machine given in Fig. 1.50 and let $A = \{q_i | 1 \leq i \leq 6\}$. Find a uniform experiment for A of length ≤ 15.

EXERCISE 5. Write the δ, λ matrix of S in Theorem 1.5 for $n = 6$.

EXERCISE 6. A machine is said to be *input-independent* if $\lambda(p, I)$ is independent of I in Σ. Show that Lemma 1.7 holds for the class of input-independent machines with the number $\sum_{n-k+r}^{n-1} i$ replaced by $\sum_{n-k+r}^{n-1} i - (k - r - 1)$.

	I^1		I^2	
q_1	q_2	0	q_1	0
q_2	q_3	1	q_3	0
q_3	q_4	0	q_3	0
q_4	q_5	0	q_4	0
q_5	q_3	0	q_1	0

FIGURE 1.49

	I^1		I^2	
q_1	q_2	0	q_6	0
q_2	q_5	0	q_5	0
q_3	q_4	1	q_6	0
q_4	q_3	1	q_5	0
q_5	q_6	0	q_5	0
q_6	q_5	0	q_3	0

FIGURE 1.50

EXERCISE 7. Show that Theorem 1.5 holds for the class of input-independent machines with the number $(2n - k)(k - 1)/2$ replaced by $(2n - k)(k - 1)/2 - (k - 2)$. [*Hint:* To show that this number is the best possible consider the following sequential machine T.

$$K = \{q_i | 1 \le i \le n\}, \qquad \Sigma = \{I^i | 1 \le i \le n - 2\},$$

and

$$\Delta = \{0, 1\}.$$

δ is the same as in Theorem 1.5. $\lambda(q_n, I) = 1$ for each input I and $\lambda(q_i, I) = 0$ otherwise.]

Unsolved Problem. Given an experiment $E = \{J(p) | p \text{ in } A\}$ for A, let

$$L(E) = \sum_{p \text{ in } A} L[J(p)],$$

where $L[J(p)]$ denotes the length of $J(p)$. Find the smallest integer $L(n, k)$ with the following property: For each distinguished machine S with n states and each set A of k states in S, there exists an experiment E for A such that $L(E) \le L(n, k)$.

The number $L(n, k)/k$ satisfies the following condition: For each distinguished machine S with n states and each set A of k states in S, there exists an experiment E for A so that the average length of the tapes used in the experiment is at most $L(n, k)/k$, and for some such S and A, and for each experiment E for A, the average length of the tapes used in E is at least $L(n, k)/k$.

1.6 History. Sequential machines are first defined in [M3]. There the output is independent of the input and is a function only of the state. This restriction is removed in [M2]. Sequential machines are also implicit in the work of Huffman [H2] dealing with the analysis and synthesis of sequential switching circuits. The reduction technique leading to minimal-state machines is found in [H2] for sequential switching circuits, and is implicit in [M3]. It is stated explicitly in [M2]. Strongly connected machines are discussed in [M3]. Experiments are first discussed in [M3]. Uniform experiments are introduced in [G2]. The attainment of the best bound for experiments is found in [K1] and for uniform experiments, in [H1].

CHAPTER 2

INCOMPLETE SEQUENTIAL MACHINES

In the previous chapter we considered *complete* sequential machines. The adjective "complete" refers to the fact that for each state q and each input I, the next state $\delta(q, I)$ and the output $\lambda(q, I)$ both exist; that is, the machine is completely specified. In this chapter we consider incomplete sequential machines. These differ from complete sequential machines in that there may be some states q and some inputs I for which either $\delta(q, I)$ or $\lambda(q, I)$ is not defined. Such machines arise in synthesis when, in the course of designing a (possibly complete) machine, it is found that δ and λ need not be completely specified in order to satisfy the specifications. The incompleteness is essential if a machine is to be obtained which satisfies the specifications and has the fewest number of states possible.

2.1 Preliminaries. We now define incomplete sequential machines and introduce the minimal-state problem.

Definition 2.1. By an *incomplete sequential machine* S is meant a 5-tuple $(K_S, \Sigma_S, \Delta_S, \delta_S, \lambda_S)$ with the following properties:

(i) K_S is a finite nonempty set (of "states");

(ii) Σ_S is a finite nonempty set (of "inputs");

(iii) Δ_S is a finite nonempty set (of "outputs");

(iv) δ_S (the "next-state" function) is a mapping from a *subset* of $K_S \times \Sigma_S$ into K_S;

(v) λ_S (the "output" function) is a mapping from a *subset* of $K_S \times \Sigma_S$ into Δ_S.

Axioms (iv) and (v) assert that in an incomplete machine there may exist states q and inputs I for which $\delta(q, I)$ is undefined, and states q and inputs I for which $\lambda(q, I)$ is undefined.

Unless otherwise stated, in this chapter the phrase "machine" or "sequential machine" is to mean "incomplete sequential machine."

The same notation, conventions, etc., that are used for complete machines are to be applied to incomplete machines. Thus an incomplete machine is represented by a δ, λ matrix and a state graph.

The extension of δ and λ from inputs to tapes is not as straightforward as in the complete machine case. The question is how to define $\delta(q, I_1 \ldots I_k)$ and $\lambda(q, I_1 \ldots I_k)$ when some of the intermediate states and outputs are

43

not defined. Definition 2.2 below rules out the existence of δ and λ unless all intermediate states and outputs respectively exist.

Definition 2.2. Let $I_1 \ldots I_k$ be a tape. $\lambda(x, I_1 \ldots I_k)$ is said to exist if each output $\lambda(x_1, I_1), \ldots, \lambda(x_k, I_k)$, and each state $x_1 = x$ and $x_{i+1} = \delta(x_i, I_i)$ for $i < k$ exists; and $\lambda(x, I_1 \ldots I_k)$, when it exists, is defined to be the output sequence $\lambda(x_1, I_1)\lambda(x_2, I_2) \ldots \lambda(x_k, I_k)$. $\delta(x, I_1 \ldots I_k)$ is said to exist if each state $x_1 = x$ and $x_{i+1} = \delta(x_i, I_i)$ for $i \leq k$ exists; and when $\delta(x, I_1 \ldots I_k)$ exists, it is defined to be the state x_{k+1}.

Observe that the equation

$$\lambda(x, I_1 \ldots I_k) = \lambda(x, I_1 \ldots I_j)\lambda[\delta(x, I_1 \ldots I_j), I_{j+1} \ldots I_k]$$

holds whenever either side exists. Similarly the equation

$$\delta(x, I_1 \ldots I_k) = \delta[\delta(x, I_1 \ldots I_j), I_{j+1} \ldots I_k]$$

holds whenever either side exists.*

Definition 2.3. A tape J is said to be *applicable* to a state q if $\lambda(q, J)$ exists.

EXAMPLE 1. Let S be the machine in Fig. 2.1. Then

(i) $\delta(q_1, I^2I^1I^1I^2) = \delta(q_3, I^1I^1I^2)$, which does not exist;

(ii) $\delta(q_2, I^1I^2I^2I^2I^2) = q_3$;

(iii) $\lambda(q_2, I^1I^2I^2I^2I^2)$ does not exist;

(iv) $\lambda(q_1, I^1) = 0$;

(v) $\lambda(q_1, I^1I^2)$ does not exist.

EXERCISE 1. Let S be the machine in Fig. 2.2.

(i) $\delta(q_1, I^1I^2I^2I^3) = ?$

(ii) $\delta(q_2, I^3I^2I^3) = ?$

(iii) $\lambda(q_2, I^3I^2I^3) = ?$

We shall formulate a number of concepts and prove a number of results for incomplete sequential machines which are analogous to corresponding concepts and results for complete sequential machines. The differences that arise are, of course, due to the existence of blanks in the δ, λ matrix. In order to guarantee the existence of the appropriate outputs and next states, we shall find that concepts about incomplete sequential machines

---

* See exercise 2 of Section 1.1.

	I^1	I^2
q_1	0	q_3 1
q_2	q_1	q_1 1
q_3	2	q_2

FIGURE 2.1

	I^1	I^2	I^3
q_1	q_2 0	q_1	q_2 1
q_2	1	q_3 0	q_1 1
q_3	q_3 0	q_2 1	0

FIGURE 2.2

	I^1	I^2
p_1	p_2 E^1	E^2
p_2	p_1	p_1 E^2

FIGURE 2.3

	I^1	I^2	I^3
q_1	q_1 E^1	q_1 E^2	E^3

FIGURE 2.4

are more complicated in the sense of having more conditions attached to them. Proofs are usually at least twice as long as corresponding ones for complete sequential machines. This is because there are more conditions to verify in the conclusion.

In comparing the work between two states of complete machines, it is sufficient to study equivalence between states. For incomplete machines a more general concept is needed.

Notation. Let S and T be sequential machines. For states p in S and q in T, by $p \leq q$ is meant that each tape J which is applicable to p is applicable to q and, in addition, $\lambda_S(p, J) = \lambda_T(q, J)$. By $S \leq T$ is meant that to each state p in S there is a state q in T such that $p \leq q$.

For states p in S and q in T, the intuitive meaning of $p \leq q$ is that machine T, starting at q, does everything that machine S, starting at p, does. The intuitive meaning of $S \leq T$ is that machine T does everything that machine S does.

EXAMPLE 2. Let S and T be the machines in Figs. 2.3 and 2.4, respectively. Then $p_1 \leq q_1$.

EXERCISE 2. Let S and T be complete machines such that $\Sigma_S = \Sigma_T$. For states p in S and q in T show that $p \leq q$ if and only if $p \equiv q$.

The following problem, called the *minimization problem*, is of concern to us and is to be investigated. Given a sequential machine S, find a sequential machine T such that

(1) $S \leq T$,

(2) for each sequential machine Y, if $S \leq Y$ then $\#(K_T) \leq \#(K_Y)$.

A sequential machine T satisfying (1) and (2) is said to be a *minimal-state machine of S.*

EXAMPLE 3.   The machine in Fig. 2.4 is a minimal-state machine of the one shown in Fig. 2.3.

We shall find that, in contrast to complete machines, there frequently is more than one minimal-state machine of an incomplete machine S. While it is easy to find a solution to the minimization problem when the machine is complete, it is vastly more difficult when the machine is incomplete. In fact, there is still no completely satisfactory procedure for finding a solution in the incomplete case.

2.2 Results on $\leq$.   Basic properties of the "$\leq$" relation are now derived. Among them is a finite procedure for determining all pairs of states p and q for which $p \leq q$.

Lemma 2.1.*   Let p be a state in S and q in T such that $p \leq q$. If $\delta_S(p, J)$, $\delta_T(q, J)$, and $\lambda_S(p, J)$ all exist for a given tape J, then $\delta_S(p, J) \leq \delta_T(q, J)$.

Proof.   Let J_1 be any tape which is applicable to the state $\delta_S(p, J)$. Then

$$\lambda_S(p, J)\,\lambda_S[\delta_S(p, J), J_1] = \lambda_S(p, JJ_1)$$
$$= \lambda_T(q, JJ_1)$$
$$= \lambda_T(q, J)\,\lambda_T[\delta_T(q, J), J_1]$$
$$= \lambda_S(p, J)\,\lambda_T[\delta_T(q, J), J_1].$$

Hence $\lambda_S[\delta_S(p, J), J_1] = \lambda_T[\delta_T(q, J), J_1]$. Thus $\delta_S(p, J) \leq \delta_T(q, J)$.

In order to derive a finite procedure which determines all states p and q in the same or different machines for which $p \leq q$, we need a concept analogous to $\overset{k}{\equiv}$ in Chapter 1.

Notation.   Let S and T be sequential machines. For each pair of states x in S and y in T and each positive integer k, the relation $(x; y; k)$ is said to hold if for each tape J, of length $t \leq k$, which is applicable to x, the following are true:

(i) J is applicable to y and $\lambda_S(x, J) = \lambda_T(y, J)$;

and

(ii)   if $\delta_S(x, J)$ exists, then $\delta_T(y, J)$ exists.

---

* Compare with Lemma 1.1.

It is relatively easy to derive the desired procedure in terms of $(x; y; k)$.

Lemma 2.2. (a) If $(x; y; k)$ holds, then $(x; y; i)$ holds for each positive integer i, $i \leq k$.
(b) Suppose that $(x; y; k)$ holds. If J is any tape of length $i < k$, applicable to x, for which both $p = \delta_S(x, J)$ and $q = \delta_T(y, J)$ exist, then $(p; q; k - i)$ holds.

EXERCISE 1. Prove Lemma 2.2.

Lemma 2.3. Let S and T be sequential machines. Denote by R_1 the set consisting of all ordered pairs (x, y) of states x in S and y in T such that for each input I applicable to x

(i) I is applicable to y and $\lambda_S(x, I) = \lambda_T(y, I)$, and

(ii)   if $\delta_S(x, I)$ exists, then $\delta_T(y, I)$ exists.

For each positive integer k let R_{k+1} denote the set of all ordered pairs (x, y) in R_k such that

(iii) if I is an input applicable to x for which $\delta_S(x, I)$ exists, then $\big(\delta_S(x, I), \delta_T(y, I)\big)$ is in R_k.

Then

(a)   each R_k consists of those pairs (x, y) of states x in S and y in T for which $(x; y; k)$ holds;

(b)   if $R_k = R_{k+1}$ for some integer k, then $R_t = R_k$ for each integer $t \geq k$.

Proof. (a) The conclusion is obvious if $k = 1$. Continuing by induction, suppose that the conclusion is true for $k \leq t$. It suffices to show that it is true for $k = t + 1$.
First assume that (x, y) is in R_{t+1}. Since (x, y) is in R_t, $(x; y; t)$ holds by the induction hypothesis. Let $I_1 J$ be any tape of length $t + 1$, I_1 in Σ_S, which is applicable to x. By Lemma 2.2, $(x; y; 1)$ holds. As I_1 is applicable to x, $\lambda(x, I_1) = \lambda(y, I_1)$. Since (x, y) is in R_{t+1} and $I_1 J$ is applicable to x, it follows that $\delta(x, I_1) = x_1$ exists. Thus $\delta(y, I_1) = y_1$ exists. By (iii), (x_1, y_1) is in R_t. Then by the induction hypothesis, $(x_1; y_1; t)$ holds. Therefore $\lambda(x_1, J) = \lambda(y_1, J)$. Then

$$\lambda(x, I_1 J) = \lambda(x, I_1)\lambda(x_1, J) = \lambda(y, I_1)\lambda(y_1, J) = \lambda(y, I_1 J).$$

Suppose, in addition, that $\delta(x, I_1 J)$ exists. Then $\delta(x, I_1 J) = \delta(x_1, J)$ exists. Since $(x_1; y_1; t)$ holds, $\delta(y_1, J) = \delta(y, I_1 J)$ exists. Therefore $(x; y; t + 1)$ holds.

	I^1		I^2	
p_1	p_2	3	p_5	
p_2	p_1	4		
p_3	p_4	3	p_4	1
p_4	p_5	4		
p_5	p_6	3	p_6	2
p_6	p_3	4		

FIGURE 2.5

	I^1		I^2	
p_1	p_1	1		
p_2	p_3	1	p_4	2
p_3	p_2	1	p_3	
p_4	p_4	1	p_1	1

FIGURE 2.6

Now suppose that $(x; y; t + 1)$ holds. Then $(x; y; t)$ holds. By the induction hypothesis, (x, y) is in R_t. Let I be any input applicable to x such that $\delta(x, I)$ exists. As (x, y) is in R_t, (x_1, y_1) exists where $x_1 = \delta(x, I)$ and $y_1 = \delta(y, I)$. Since $(x; y; t + 1)$ holds, $(x_1; y_1; t)$ holds by (b) of Lemma 2.2. By the induction hypothesis then, (x_1, y_1) is in R_t. Hence (x, y) is in R_{t+1}.

(b) Suppose that $R_k = R_{k+1}$. Using induction, assume that $R_k = R_{k+r}$ for $r \le j$, $j \ge 1$. It suffices to show that $R_k = R_{k+j+1}$. To this end let (x, y) be in $R_k = R_{k+j}$. Let I be an input applicable to x for which $\delta(x, I)$ exists. Since (x, y) is in R_{k+j}, it follows that $\big(\delta(x, I), \delta(y, I)\big)$ is in $R_{k+j-1} = R_k = R_{k+j}$. Thus (x, y) is in R_{k+j+1}, that is, $R_k = R_{k+j} = R_{k+j+1}$.

EXAMPLE 1. Let $S = T$ be the machine in Fig. 2.5. Then

$$R_1 = Q \cup \{(p_1, p_3), (p_1, p_5), (p_2, p_4), (p_2, p_6),$$

$$(p_4, p_2), (p_4, p_6), (p_6, p_2), (p_6, p_4)\},$$

$$\text{where } Q = \{(p_i, p_i) | 1 \le i \le 6\};$$

$$R_2 = Q \cup \{(p_1, p_3), (p_1, p_5), (p_2, p_4), (p_2, p_6)\};$$

and

$$R_3 = R_2.$$

EXERCISE 2. Let $S = T$ be the machine in Fig. 2.6. Find all pairs (x, y) of states x in S and y in T for which $R_k = R_{k+1}$.

EXERCISE 3. Let S and T be the machines in Figs. 2.7 and 2.8, respectively. Find all pairs (x, y) of states x in S and y in T for which $R_k = R_{k+1}$.

	I^1	I^2
p_1	p_2 E^1	
p_2	E^2	
p_3	p_5	E^1
p_4	p_2	p_1
p_5	p_3	p_4 E^1

FIGURE 2.7

	I^1	I^2
q_1	E^2	q_4
q^2		E^1
q_3	q_5 E^1	
q_4	q_1 E^1	E^2
q_5	q_1 E^2	E^1

FIGURE 2.8

One more concept is needed in order to describe an algorithm for determining all pairs (x, y) of states x in S and y in T for which $x \leq y$.

Definition 2.4. A state p in a sequential machine is called *output-empty* if there is no input which is applicable to p.

A state which is output-empty does no work measured by inputs versus outputs. In a sense, it is a degenerate state with respect to those properties involving the phrase "applicable tape." Because of this it is convenient to remove all output-empty states from a machine and deal with the remaining machine.

Notation. For each sequential machine $S = (K, \Sigma, \Delta, \delta, \lambda)$, let $S_* = (K_*, \Sigma, \Delta, \delta_*, \lambda_*)$, where

(i) K_* is the set of states of S which are not output-empty,

(ii) λ_* is the function λ restricted to $K_* \times \Sigma$, and

(iii) for (q, I) in $K_* \times \Sigma$, $\delta_*(q, I) = \delta(q, I)$ if $\delta(q, I)$ is in K_*, and δ_* is undefined otherwise.

EXERCISES. Prove each of the following.

4. S_* has no output-empty states.

5. A tape J is applicable to a state p in S if and only if J is applicable to p considered in S_*.

6. If a tape J is applicable to a state p in S, then $\lambda(p, J) = \lambda_*(p, J)$.

7. Let S and T be sequential machines. Let p be in S_* and q in T. If $p \leq q$, p considered in S_*, then $p \leq q$, p considered in S.

8. $S \leq S_*$ and $S_* \leq S$.

Theorem 2.1. Let S and T be sequential machines. For each integer i let R_i be defined between S_* and T as in Lemma 2.3. Then

(a) $x \leq y$, x considered in S, if and only if either x is output-empty or $x \leq y$, x considered in S_*;

  (b) there exists an integer k so that $R_k = R_{k+1}$;

  (c) $x \leq y$, x considered in S_*, if and only if (x, y) is in R_k, where $R_k = R_{k+1}$.

Proof. (a) If x is an output-empty state then, from the definition of $\leq$, $x \leq y$ for every state y in T. If $x \leq y$, x in S_*, then, by exercise 7, $x \leq y$, x considered in S. Thus the "only if" is verified.

Suppose that $x \leq y$, x in S. Either x is output-empty or not. If not, let J be a tape applicable to x considered in S_*. By exercises 5 and 6, J is applicable to x in S and $\lambda(x, J) = \lambda_*(x, J)$. As $x \leq y$, x considered in S, $\lambda(x, J) = \lambda(y, J)$. Thus

$$\lambda_*(x, J) = \lambda(y, J),$$

whence $x \leq y$, x considered in S_*.

  (b) From the definition, $R_{i+1} \subseteq R_i$ for each i. Also, as K_* is finite, so is R_1. If R_{i+1} were to be a proper subset of R_i for an infinite number of integers i, then R_1 would be infinite, a contradiction. Thus there is an integer k such that $R_{k+1} = R_k$.

  (c) Suppose that (x, y) is in R_k, where $R_k = R_{k+1}$. By (b) of Lemma 2.3, (x, y) is in R_t for every $t \geq k$. By (a) of Lemma 2.3, $(x; y; t)$ holds for every $t \geq k$. By (a) of Lemma 2.2, $(x; y; j)$ holds for every j. Thus $x \leq y$, x considered in S_*.

Suppose that $x \leq y$, x considered in S_*. To complete the proof of (c) it is sufficient to show that (x, y) is in R_t for every t. Accordingly, let J be any tape applicable to x. Since $x \leq y$, then J is applicable to y and $\lambda_*(x, J) = \lambda(y, J)$. In addition, suppose that $\delta_*(x, J)$ exists. Since $\delta_*(x, J)$ is not an output-empty state, there exists an input I applicable to $\delta_*(x, J)$. Hence JI is applicable to x. Since $x \leq y$, it follows that JI is applicable to y. Then $\delta(y, J)$ exists. Therefore $(x; y; t)$ holds for every t. By (a) of Lemma 2.3, (x, y) is in R_t for every t.

Theorem 2.1 yields a finite procedure for finding the set of all pairs (x, y) of states x in S and y in T for which $x \leq y$. The procedure consists of

  (i) finding all output-empty states of S,

  (ii) forming all pairs (p, q) of states q in T and p output-empty in S,

  (iii) constructing S_*; and

  (iv) calculating R_i until $R_{k+1} = R_k$.

The desired set consists of those pairs referred to in (ii) as well as all pairs in R_k of (iv).

EXAMPLE 2. Let $S = T$ be the machine given in Fig. 2.9. The only state in S which is output-empty is p_3. Thus $p_3 \leq p_i$, $1 \leq i \leq 5$. The

	I^1	I^2
p_1	p_4 E^1	p_3 E^2
p_2	p_5	E^1
p_3	p_4	p_2
p_4	p_3 E^2	p_3 E^1
p_5	p_2 E^1	E^2

FIGURE 2.9

	I^1	I^2
p_1	p_4 E^1	E^2
p_2	p_5	E^1
p_4	E^2	E^1
p_5	p_2 E^1	E^2

FIGURE 2.10

	I^1	I^2
p_1	p_3 E^1	p_5 E^2
p_2	p_5	p_1 E^1
p_3	p_3 E^1	
p_4	p_1 E^1	p_1 E^2
p_5	p_5	p_6
p_6	p_4 E^1	p_4 E^1

FIGURE 2.11

	I^1	I^2	I^3
p_1	p_6 E^1		
p_2	p_3 E^1		p_8
p_3	p_3 E^1	E^2	p_1 E^2
p_4		p_4	p_2
p_5	p_4	p_4 E^2	p_7 E^2
p_6	p_2 E^1	E^2	E^2
p_7	p_3		p_5
p_8	E^2	E^2	p_6

FIGURE 2.12

machine S_* is in Fig. 2.10. Calculation of the R_i yields

$$R_1 = Q \cup \{(p_1, p_5),\ (p_2, p_4),\ (p_5, p_1)\},$$

$$\text{where } Q = \{(p_i, p_i)|1 \leq i \leq 5\};$$

$$R_2 = Q \cup \{(p_2, p_4),\ (p_5, p_1)\};$$

and

$$R_3 = R_2.$$

The set of those pairs (x, y) of states in S for which $x \leq y$ is

$$R_2 \cup \{(p_3, p_i)|1 \leq i \leq 5\}.$$

EXERCISE 9. Find the set of those pairs (x, y) of states in $S = T$ for which $x \leq y$, where S is given in (a) Fig. 2.11, (b) Fig. 2.12.

	I^1	I^2
p_1	$p_3\ E^1$	
p_2	$p_4\ E^1$	$p_3\ E^2$
p_3	p_2	p_4
p_4	E^1	
p_5	p_1	E^1

FIGURE 2.13

	I^1	I^2
q_1	$q_2\ E^1$	E^2
q_2	E^1	q_3
q_3	E^1	
q_4	q_1	$q_2\ E^1$

FIGURE 2.14

	I^1	I^2
p_1	$p_2\ E^1$	
p_2	p_3	E^2
p_3	E^1	
p_4	p_2	
p_5	p_3	$p_4\ E^1$

FIGURE 2.15

	I^1	I^2	I^3
q_1		$q_1\ E^2$	$q_2\ E^2$
q_2	$q_2\ E^1$		$q_1\ E^3$
q_3		E^1	$q_4\ E^1$
q_4	E^2	E^2	$q_1\ E^2$

FIGURE 2.16

EXERCISE 10. Find all pairs (x, y) of states x in S and y in T for which $x \leq y$ when S and T are (a) in Figs. 2.13 and 2.14, respectively, and (b) in Figs. 2.15 and 2.16, respectively.

It is natural to inquire as to the smallest integer k for which $R_k = R_{k+1}$. The smallest possible bound for the general case is derived in Theorems 2.2 and 2.3, according as $S = T$ or S and T are different. In preparation for Theorem 2.2 the following result, which is the counterpart for incomplete machines of (e) of Lemma 1.2, is needed.

Lemma 2.4. Let S be a sequential machine with $n \geq 2$ states. If $(p; q; n - 1)$ and $(q; p; n - 1)$ both hold for the states p and q in S, then $(p; q; k)$ and $(q; p; k)$ both hold for every positive integer k.

Proof. For each positive integer j and each pair of states x and y write $x\ E_j\ y$ if $(x; y; j)$ and $(y; x; j)$ both hold. Clearly each E_j is an equivalence relation. Denote by D_j the set of equivalence classes generated by E_j.

From the definition of E_j and (a) of Lemma 2.2, the following becomes obvious.

(1) If x and y are in the same equivalence class of D_{j+1}, then x and y are in the same equivalence class of D_j. Thus each equivalence class in D_{j+1} is a subclass of an equivalence class in D_j.

Suppose that $E_k = E_{k+1}$ for some positive integer k. Using induction, assume that $E_k = E_{k+j}$ for $j \leq t$. If $xE_{k+t+1}y$, then clearly $xE_{k+t}y$. Suppose that $xE_{k+t}y$. Then $(x; y; k+t)$ holds. By (a) of Lemma 2.3, for each input I applicable to either x or y, $(x; y; k+t-1)$, $(\delta(x, I);$ $\delta(y, I); k+t-1)$, $(y; x; k+t-1)$, and $(\delta(y, I); \delta(x, I); k+t-1)$ hold. Then $xE_{k+t-1}y$ and $\delta(x, I)E_{k+t-1}\delta(y, I)$ hold. Since $E_{k+t-1} = E_{k+t}$, then $xE_{k+t}y$ and $\delta(x, I)E_{k+t}\delta(y, I)$. Hence $(x; y; k+t)$, $(y; x; k+t)$, $(\delta(x, I); \delta(y, I); k+t)$, and $(\delta(y, I); \delta(x, I); k+t)$ hold. By (a) of Lemma 2.3, $(x; y; k+t+1)$ and $(y; x; k+t+1)$ hold. Then $xE_{k+t+1}y$. Thus $E_k = E_{k+t} = E_{k+t+1}$. Therefore,

(2) if $E_k = E_{k+1}$ for some integer k, then $E_k = E_{k+j}$ for all $j \geq 0$.

Suppose that $\#(D_1) = 1$. Then xE_1y for all states x and y. Let I be an input applicable to x for which $\delta(x, I)$ exists. Then $\delta(y, I)$ exists. Since $\#(D_1) = 1$, then $\delta(x, I)E_1\delta(y, I)$. By (a) of Lemma 2.3 (applied twice), xE_2y. Thus

(3) $E_1 = E_2$ if $\#(D_1) = 1$.

Suppose that $\#(D_1) > 1$. By (1), $\#(D_1) \leq \#(D_2) \leq \ldots$. Since each equivalence class in each D_i contains at least one state, $\#(D_i) \leq \#(K_S) = n$ for each i. Then there exists an integer such that $\#(D_i) = \#(D_{i+1})$, hence a smallest such integer, say s. Then $D_s = D_{s+1}$. Since

$$1 < \#(D_1) < \#(D_2) < \cdots < \#(D_s),$$

it follows that $s + 1 \leq \#(D_s) \leq n$. Thus $s \leq n - 1$. By (2), $D_s = D_{n-1} = D_n$. Hence

(4) $D_{n-1} = D_n$ if $\#(D_1) > 1$.

From (2), (3), and (4), $D_{n-1} = D_n = D_{n+t}$ for all $t \geq 0$. Hence, if $(p; q; n - 1)$ and $(q; p; n - 1)$ hold, then $(p; q; n + t)$ and $(q; p; n + t)$ hold for all $t \geq 0$. From (a) of Lemma 2.2 it follows that $(p; q; j)$ and $(q; p; j)$ hold for all j.

Theorem 2.2. (a) Let S be a sequential machine with no output-empty states. Let p_1 and q_1 be any states in S. Then $p_1 \leq q_1$ if and only if

$$\left(p_1; q_1; \frac{n(n-1)}{2} + n - 1\right)$$

holds, where $n = \#(K_S)$. (b) The number $n(n-1)/2 + n - 1$ is the smallest possible number in the general case.

Proof. Part (a). The "only if" results from the fact that if S has no output-empty states and $x \leq y$, then $(x; y; t)$ holds for all t.

Now let S, n, p_1, and q_1 satisfy the "if" of (a). Let $d = n(n - 1)/2$. Obviously it may be assumed that $p_1 \neq q_1$. By hypothesis, $(p_1; q_1; k)$ is true for $k = d + n - 1$ and thus for $k \leq d + n - 1$. Using induction, assume that $(p_1; q_1; k)$ is true for $k \leq t$, where $t \geq d + n - 1 \geq d + 1$. It is therefore sufficient to show that $(p_1; q_1; t + 1)$ is true.

To do this, let $J = I_1 \ldots I_{t+1}$ be any tape, of length $t + 1$, which is applicable to p_1. Let $E_1 \ldots E_{t+1} = \lambda(p_1, J)$. Since $(p_1; q_1; t)$ holds for each $i \leq t$,

$$\lambda(q_1, I_1 \ldots I_i) = \lambda(p_1, I_1 \ldots I_i) = E_1 \ldots E_i.$$

For $i \leq t - 1$ let $p_{i+1} = \delta(p_1, I_1 \ldots I_i)$ and let $q_{i+1} = \delta(q_1, I_1 \ldots I_i)$. There are t ordered pairs (p_i, q_i).

The gist of this portion of the proof is the following. For t large enough, namely at least $n(n - 1)/2 + 1$, there exist u and v, $u < v$, so that $\{p_u, q_u\} = \{p_v, q_v\}$. The part of the tape from I_u to I_{v-1} is removed from J to produce a smaller tape. If $p_u = p_v$ and $q_u = q_v$, then using the induction hypothesis, one directly obtains the existence of q_{t+1} and $\lambda(q_{t+1}, I_{t+1}) = E_{t+1}$. If $p_u = q_v$ and $q_u = p_v$, then the last $n - 1$ inputs added to the first $n(n - 1)/2$ yield both $(p_v; q_v; n - 1)$ and $(q_v; p_v; n - 1)$. From this result it follows that q_{t+1} exists and

$$\lambda(q_{t+1}, I_{t+1}) = E_{t+1}.$$

The formal proof proceeds as follows. Suppose that $p_i = q_i$ for some $i \leq t$. Since $p_1 \neq q_1$, $i > 1$. Then

$$\begin{aligned}
\lambda(p_1, J) &= \lambda(p_1, I_1 \ldots I_{i-1})\lambda(p_i, I_i \ldots I_{t+1}) \\
&= \lambda(p_1, I_1 \ldots I_{i-1})\lambda(q_i, I_i \ldots I_{t+1}) \\
&= \lambda(q_1, I_1 \ldots I_{i-1})\lambda(q_i, I_i \ldots I_{t+1}) \\
&= \lambda(q_1, J).
\end{aligned}$$

Suppose that $p_i \neq q_i$ for each $i \leq t$. Since S has n states and there are only $d = n(n - 1)/2 < t$ different combinations of states of S taken two at a time, two alternatives arise.

(1) There exist two integers u and v, with $u < v \leq d + 1 \leq t$, for which $p_u = p_v$ and $q_u = q_v$. The tape $I_1 \ldots I_{u-1}I_vI_{v+1} \ldots I_{t+1}$ is of length $\leq t$, it being understood that the tape is actually $I_v \ldots I_{t+1}$ if $u = 1$. Since

$$E_1 \ldots E_{t+1} = \lambda(p_1, J) = E_1 \ldots E_{v-1}\lambda(p_v, I_v \ldots I_{t+1}),$$

it follows that

$$\lambda(p_v, I_v \ldots I_{t+1}) = E_v \ldots E_{t+1}.$$

Since $p_u = p_v$,

$$\lambda(p_1, I_1 \ldots I_{u-1}I_v \ldots I_{t+1}) = E_1 \ldots E_{u-1}\lambda(p_u, I_v \ldots I_{t+1})$$
$$= E_1 \ldots E_{u-1}\lambda(p_v, I_v \ldots I_{t+1})$$
$$= E_1 \ldots E_{u-1}E_v \ldots E_{t+1}.$$

By assumption, $(p_1; q_1; k)$ holds for $k \leq t$. Thus

$$\lambda(q_1, I_1 \ldots I_{u-1}I_v \ldots I_{t+1}) = \lambda(p_1, I_1 \ldots I_{u-1}I_v \ldots I_{t+1})$$
$$= E_1 \ldots E_{u-1}E_v \ldots E_{t+1}.$$

Also,

$$\lambda(q_1, I_1 \ldots I_{u-1}I_v \ldots I_{t+1}) = \lambda(q_1, I_1 \ldots I_{u-1})\lambda(q_u, I_v \ldots I_{t+1})$$
$$= E_1 \ldots E_{u-1}\lambda(q_v, I_v \ldots I_{t+1}),$$

since $q_u = q_v$. Therefore $\lambda(q_v, I_v \ldots I_{t+1}) = E_v \ldots E_{t+1}$. Then

$$\lambda(q_1, J) = E_1 \ldots E_{v-1}\lambda(q_v, I_v \ldots I_{t+1})$$
$$= E_1 \ldots E_{v-1}E_v \ldots E_{t+1}.$$

Hence $\lambda(p_1, J) = \lambda(q_1, J)$.

(2) There exist two integers u and v, with $u < v \leq d + n - 1 \leq t$ for which $p_u = q_v$ and $q_u = p_v$. Let $a = u, v$. Since $(p_1; q_1; t)$ holds, by (b) of Lemma 2.2, $(p_a; q_a; t - a + 1)$ holds. Since $a \leq d + 1$ and $d + n - 1 \leq t$,

$$(p_a; q_a; t - (d + 1) + 1) = (p_a; q_a; t - d)$$

holds. Thus $(p_a; q_a; n - 1)$ holds. Therefore

$$(p_v; q_v; n - 1) \quad \text{and} \quad (p_u; q_u; n - 1) = (q_v; p_v; n - 1)$$

both hold. By Lemma 2.4, $(p_v; q_v; j)$ and $(q_v; p_v; j)$ are both true for all positive integers j. Since $\lambda(p_v, I_v \ldots I_{t+1})$ exists, $\lambda(q_v, I_v \ldots I_{t+1})$ exists and

$$\lambda(p_v, I_v \ldots I_{t+1}) = \lambda(q_v, I_v \ldots I_{t+1}).$$

Then

$$\lambda(p_1, J) = \lambda(p_1, I_1 \ldots I_{v-1})\lambda(p_v, I_v \ldots I_{t+1})$$
$$= \lambda(q_1, I_1 \ldots I_{v-1})\lambda(q_v, I_v \ldots I_{t+1})$$
$$= \lambda(q_1, J).$$

In both (1) and (2), therefore, $\lambda(p_1, J) = \lambda(q_1, J)$.

Now assume that for some tape $J = I_1 \ldots I_{t+1}$ which is applicable to p_1, $\delta(p_1, J)$ exists. If $p_i = q_i$ for some $i \leq t$, then as is easily seen, $\delta(q_1, J)$ exists [and also equals $\delta(p_1, J)$]. Suppose that $p_u = p_v$ and $q_u = q_v$ for two integers u and v such that $u < v \leq d + n - 1 \leq t$. Then

$$\lambda(p_1, J) = \lambda(p_1, I_1 \ldots I_{v-1})\lambda(p_v, I_v \ldots I_{t+1})$$
$$= \lambda(p_1, I_1 \ldots I_{v-1})\lambda(p_u, I_v \ldots I_{t+1}).$$

Thus

$$\lambda(p_1, I_1 \ldots I_{u-1}I_v \ldots I_{t+1}) = \lambda(p_1, I_1 \ldots I_{u-1})\lambda(p_u, I_v \ldots I_{t+1})$$

exists. Now

$$\delta(p_1, J) = \delta(p_v, I_v \ldots I_{t+1})$$
$$= \delta(p_u, I_v \ldots I_{t+1})$$
$$= \delta(p_1, I_1 \ldots I_{u-1}I_v \ldots I_{t+1}).$$

Since $(p_1; q_1; t)$ holds and $I_1 \ldots I_{u-1}I_v \ldots I_{t+1}$ is a tape of length $\leq t$ applicable to p_1 for which $\delta(p_1, I_1 \ldots I_{u-1}I_v \ldots I_{t+1})$ exists, $\delta(q_1, I_1 \ldots I_{u-1}I_v \ldots I_{t+1})$ exists. Then

$$\delta(q_1, I_1 \ldots I_{u-1}I_v \ldots I_{t+1}) = \delta(q_u, I_v \ldots I_{t+1})$$
$$= \delta(q_v, I_v \ldots I_{t+1})$$
$$= \delta(q_1, J)$$

exists in this case. Finally, suppose that $p_u = q_v$ and $q_u = p_v$ for two integers u and v such that $u < v \leq d + n - 1 \leq t$. From (2), $(p_v; q_v; j)$ and $(q_v; p_v; j)$ hold for all positive integers j. Since $\delta(p_v, I_v \ldots I_{t+1}) = \delta(p_1, J)$ exists, $\delta(q_v, I_v \ldots I_{t+1}) = \delta(q_1, J)$ exists. In all cases, therefore, $\delta(q_1, J)$ exists. Hence $(p_1; q_1; t + 1)$ holds and (a) is proved.

Part (b). Let $n \geq 2$ be a given integer and let $d = n(n - 1)/2$. Define a machine S with n states labeled $z_1, \ldots, z_n$, $d + 1$ inputs labeled $I^1, \ldots, I^{d+1}$, and $d + 1$ outputs labeled $E^1, \ldots, E^{d+1}$ as follows. Let C be the set of all ordered pairs $C = \{(z_i, z_j) | 1 \leq i < j \leq n\}$. Since C contains all the combinations of the n elements z_i, taken two at a time, C has exactly $n(n - 1)/2 = d$ elements. Sequence the elements in C thus: (z_i, z_j) appears before (z_a, z_b) if $i < a$ or if $i = a$ and $j < b$. For $1 \leq i \leq d$, denote the ith term in the sequence by (p_i, q_i). Thus, for example,

$$(p_1, q_1) = (z_1, z_2),$$

$$(p_2, q_2) = (z_1, z_3), \quad \text{and} \quad (p_d, q_d) = (z_{n-1}, z_n).$$

The two functions δ and λ are defined in three stages.

Stage 1. For $k \leq d$ and $i \leq n$, let $\lambda(z_i, I^k) = E^k$. Thus, for $k \leq d$, $\lambda(z_i, I^k)$ depends only on I^k. For $i < d$, let $\delta(p_i, I^i) = p_{i+1}$ and $\delta(q_i, I^i) = q_{i+1}$. Let $\delta(p_d, I^d) = q_1$ and $\delta(q_d, I^d) = p_1$. Since $p_i \neq q_i$ for each i, δ is uniquely defined for certain of the states z_j and certain of the inputs I^k.

Stage 2. Recursively, if $\delta(z_j, I^k)$ is defined and $\delta(z_{j+1}, I^k)$ is undefined, let $\delta(z_{j+1}, I^k) = \delta(z_j, I^k)$.

Stage 3. For $k \leq d$, if $\delta(z_i, I^k)$ is still undefined, let $\delta(z_i, I^k) = z_1$. Let $\delta(z_n, I^{d+1}) = z_1$ and $\lambda(z_n, I^{d+1}) = E^{d+1}$.

Observe that $\delta(z_i, I^j)$ and $\lambda(z_i, I^j)$ are defined only for $i \leq n$ and $j \leq d$, and $i = n$ and $j = d + 1$. Thus $\delta(z_i, I^{d+1})$ and $\lambda(z_i, I^{d+1})$ are undefined for $i \leq n - 1$.

It is shown in the Appendix that $z_1 \leq z_2$ is false but

$$\left(z_1; z_2; \frac{n(n-1)}{2} + n - 2 \right)$$

holds. This shows that $n(n-1)/2 + n - 1$ is the smallest possible bound in the general case.

To illustrate the above construction, consider the case when $n = 5$. Then $d = 5 \times 4/2 = 10$. The ordered pairs, written $\binom{z_i}{z_j}$ instead of (z_i, z_j), in the proper order in the sequence are

$$\binom{z_1}{z_2} \binom{z_1}{z_3} \binom{z_1}{z_4} \binom{z_1}{z_5} \binom{z_2}{z_3} \binom{z_2}{z_4} \binom{z_2}{z_5} \binom{z_3}{z_4} \binom{z_3}{z_5} \binom{z_4}{z_5}.$$

Writing I^i above the ith term and adding $\binom{z_2}{z_1}$ to the end of the sequence, we get

$$\begin{array}{ccccccccccc} I^1 & I^2 & I^3 & I^4 & I^5 & I^6 & I^7 & I^8 & I^9 & I^{10} & \\ \binom{z_1}{z_2} & \binom{z_1}{z_3} & \binom{z_1}{z_4} & \binom{z_1}{z_5} & \binom{z_2}{z_3} & \binom{z_2}{z_4} & \binom{z_2}{z_5} & \binom{z_3}{z_4} & \binom{z_3}{z_5} & \binom{z_4}{z_5} & \binom{z_2}{z_1}. \end{array}$$

To derive the δ-function at the end of the first stage, read from left to right. The three stages in the construction of the machine S are shown in Fig. 2.17.

EXERCISE 11. Find machine S in (b) of Theorem 2.2 when $n = 6$.

As a corollary we obtain a result which improves (c) of Theorem 2.1.

Corollary. Let S be a sequential machine with no output-empty states. In the notation of Lemma 2.3, $x \leq y$ if and only if (x, y) is in

$$R_{n(n-1)/2+n-1}, \quad \text{where} \quad n = \#(K_S).$$

Furthermore, $n(n-1)/2 + n - 1$ is the smallest possible number in the general case.

	I^1	I^2	I^3	I^4	I^5	I^6	I^7	I^8	I^9	I^{10}	I^{11}
z_1	$E^1_{z_1}$	$E^2_{z_1}$	$E^3_{z_1}$	$E^4_{z_2}$	E^5	E^6	E^7	E^8	E^9	E^{10}	
z_2	$E^1_{z_3}$	E^2	E^3	E^4	$E^5_{z_2}$	$E^6_{z_2}$	$E^7_{z_3}$	E^8	E^9	E^{10}	
z_3	E^1	$E^2_{z_4}$	E^3	E^4	$E^5_{z_4}$	E^6	E^7	$E^8_{z_3}$	$E^9_{z_4}$	E^{10}	
z_4	E^1	E^2	$E^3_{z_5}$	E^4	E^5	$E^6_{z_5}$	E^7	$E^8_{z_5}$	E^9	$E^{10}_{z_2}$	
z_5	E^1	E^2	E^3	$E^4_{z_3}$	E^5	E^6	$E^7_{z_4}$	E^8	$E^9_{z_5}$	$E^{10}_{z_1}$	

	I^1	I^2	I^3	I^4	I^5	I^6	I^7	I^8	I^9	I^{10}	I^{11}
z_1	$E^1_{z_1}$	$E^2_{z_1}$	$E^3_{z_1}$	$E^4_{z_2}$	E^5	E^6	E^7	E^8	E^9	E^{10}	
z_2	$E^1_{z_3}$	$E^2_{z_1}$	$E^3_{z_1}$	$E^4_{z_2}$	$E^5_{z_2}$	$E^6_{z_2}$	$E^7_{z_3}$	E^8	E^9	E^{10}	
z_3	$E^1_{z_3}$	$E^2_{z_4}$	$E^3_{z_1}$	$E^4_{z_2}$	$E^5_{z_4}$	$E^6_{z_2}$	$E^7_{z_3}$	$E^8_{z_3}$	$E^9_{z_4}$	E^{10}	
z_4	$E^1_{z_3}$	$E^2_{z_4}$	$E^3_{z_5}$	$E^4_{z_2}$	$E^5_{z_4}$	$E^6_{z_5}$	$E^7_{z_3}$	$E^8_{z_5}$	$E^9_{z_4}$	$E^{10}_{z_2}$	
z_5	$E^1_{z_3}$	$E^2_{z_4}$	$E^3_{z_5}$	$E^4_{z_3}$	$E^5_{z_4}$	$E^6_{z_5}$	$E^7_{z_4}$	$E^8_{z_5}$	$E^9_{z_5}$	$E^{10}_{z_1}$	

	I^1	I^2	I^3	I^4	I^5	I^6	I^7	I^8	I^9	I^{10}	I^{11}
z_1	$E^1_{z_1}$	$E^2_{z_1}$	$E^3_{z_1}$	$E^4_{z_2}$	$E^5_{z_1}$	$E^6_{z_1}$	$E^7_{z_1}$	$E^8_{z_1}$	$E^9_{z_1}$	$E^{10}_{z_1}$	$E^{11}_{z_1}$
z_2	$E^1_{z_3}$	$E^2_{z_1}$	$E^3_{z_1}$	$E^4_{z_2}$	$E^5_{z_2}$	$E^6_{z_2}$	$E^7_{z_3}$	$E^8_{z_1}$	$E^9_{z_1}$	$E^{10}_{z_1}$	
z_3	$E^1_{z_3}$	$E^2_{z_4}$	$E^3_{z_1}$	$E^4_{z_2}$	$E^5_{z_4}$	$E^6_{z_2}$	$E^7_{z_3}$	$E^8_{z_3}$	$E^9_{z_4}$	$E^{10}_{z_1}$	
z_4	$E^1_{z_3}$	$E^2_{z_4}$	$E^3_{z_5}$	$E^4_{z_2}$	$E^5_{z_4}$	$E^6_{z_5}$	$E^7_{z_3}$	$E^8_{z_5}$	$E^9_{z_4}$	$E^{10}_{z_2}$	
z_5	$E^1_{z_3}$	$E^2_{z_4}$	$E^3_{z_5}$	$E^4_{z_3}$	$E^5_{z_4}$	$E^6_{z_5}$	$E^7_{z_4}$	$E^8_{z_5}$	$E^9_{z_5}$	$E^{10}_{z_1}$	

FIGURE 2.17

Unsolved problem. The proof given in the Appendix that $n(n-1)/2 + n - 1$ is the smallest possible number is complicated. Find a different machine for which it is easier to show that $n(n-1)/2 + n - 1$ is the smallest possible number.

Turning to the case in which S and T are different, we have a companion result to Theorem 2.2. The lowest number here is mn, where $n = \#(K_S)$ and $m = \#(K_T)$. The proof that this number is a bound is similar to that of (a) of Theorem 2.2. The significance of mn is that it is the number of pairs (p, q) of states p in S and q in T.

Theorem 2.3. (a) Let S and T be sequential machines with n and m states, respectively. Let S have no output-empty states. For states p_1 in S and q_1 in T, $p_1 \leq q_1$ if and only if $(p_1; q_1; nm)$ holds. (b) The number nm is the smallest possible in the general case.

Proof. (a) As in Theorem 2.2, the "only if" results from the fact that if S has no output-empty states and $x \leq y$, then $(x; y; t)$ holds for all t.

Suppose that S, T, p_1, and q_1 satisfy the "if" of (a). Then $(p_1; q_1; nm)$ holds. Using induction, assume that $(p_1; q_1; k)$ holds for each $k \leq t$, where $t \geq nm$. To prove (a) it is sufficient to show that $(p_1; q_1; t+1)$ holds.

To this end, let $J = I_1 \ldots I_{t+1}$ be any tape, of length $t + 1$, which is applicable to p_1. Let $E_1 \ldots E_{t+1} = \lambda_S(p_1, J)$. Since $(p_1; q_1; t)$ is assumed to hold,

$$\lambda_T(q_1, I_1 \ldots I_t) = \lambda_S(p_1, I_1 \ldots I_t) = E_1 \ldots E_t.$$

For $i \leq t$ let $p_{i+1} = \delta_S(p_1, I_1 \ldots I_i)$ and $q_{i+1} = \delta_T(q_1, I_1 \ldots I_i)$. Since J is applicable to p_1, then $\delta_S(p_1, I_1 \ldots I_t)$ exists. Since $(p_1; q_1; t)$ holds, $\delta_T(q_1, I_1 \ldots I_t) = q_{t+1}$ exists. There are $t + 1$ such ordered pairs (p_i, q_i). Since $\#(K_S) = n$ and $\#(K_T) = m$, there are only $nm < t + 1$ different ordered pairs (p, q) of states p in S and q in T. Hence there exist integers u and v, $u < v \leq t + 1$, so that $p_u = p_v$ and $q_u = q_v$.

Consider $\lambda_T(q_1, J)$. Since

$$E_1 \ldots E_{t+1} = \lambda_S(p_1, J) = E_1 \ldots E_{v-1}\lambda_S(p_v, I_v \ldots I_{t+1}),$$

it follows that

$$\lambda_S(p_v, I_v \ldots I_{t+1}) = E_v E_{v+1} \ldots E_{t+1}.$$

Since $p_u = p_v$,

$$\begin{aligned}
\lambda_S(p_1, I_1 \ldots I_{u-1}I_v \ldots I_{t+1}) &= E_1 \ldots E_{u-1}\lambda_S(p_u, I_v \ldots I_{t+1}) \\
&= E_1 \ldots E_{u-1}\lambda_S(p_v, I_v \ldots I_{t+1}) \\
&= E_1 \ldots E_{u-1}E_v \ldots E_{t+1}.
\end{aligned}$$

	I^1	I^2
p_1		$p_1 \quad E^2$

$(n = 1)$

	I^1	I^2
q_1	$q_1 \quad E^1$	$q_1 \quad E^1$

$(m = 1)$

	I^1	I^2
p_1	$p_2 \quad E^1$	
$\vdots$	$\vdots$	
p_{n-1}	$p_n \quad E^1$	
p_n		$p_1 \quad E^2$

$(n \geq 2)$

FIGURE 2.18

	I^1	I^2
q_1	$q_1 \quad E^1$	$q_2 \quad E^2$
$\vdots$	$\vdots$	$\vdots$
q_{m-1}	$q_{m-1} \quad E^1$	$q_m \quad E^2$
q_m	$q_m \quad E^1$	$q_1 \quad E^1$

$(m \geq 2)$

FIGURE 2.19

By assumption, $(p_1; q_1; k)$ holds for $k \leq t$. Thus

$$\lambda_T(q_1, I_1 \ldots I_{u-1}I_v \ldots I_{t+1}) = \lambda_S(p_1, I_1 \ldots I_{u-1}I_v \ldots I_{t+1})$$
$$= E_1 \ldots E_{u-1}E_v \ldots E_{t+1}.$$

Also,

$$\lambda_T(q_1, I_1 \ldots I_{u-1}I_v \ldots I_{t+1}) = \lambda_T(q_1, I_1 \ldots I_{u-1})\lambda_T(q_u, I_v \ldots I_{t+1})$$
$$= E_1 \ldots E_{u-1}\lambda_T(q_v, I_v \ldots I_{t+1}),$$

since $q_u = q_v$. Therefore

$$\lambda_T(q_v, I_v \ldots I_{t+1}) = E_v \ldots E_{t+1}.$$

Then

$$\lambda_T(q_1, J) = E_1 \ldots E_{v-1}\lambda_T(q_v, I_v \ldots I_{t+1})$$
$$= E_1 \ldots E_{v-1}E_v \ldots E_{t+1}$$
$$= \lambda_S(p_1, J).$$

Thus (i) in the notation (preceding Lemma 2.2) of $(p_1; q_1; t + 1)$ holds.

Suppose that J is applicable to p_1 and $\delta_S(p_1, J)$ exists, with $p_u = p_v$ and $q_u = q_v, u < v \leq t + 1$. As above, we see that $I_1 \ldots I_{u-1}I_v \ldots I_{t+1}$ is applicable to p_1 and $\delta_S(p_1, I_1 \ldots I_{u-1}I_v \ldots I_{t+1})$ exists. Since

$(p_1; q_1; t)$ holds, $\delta_T(q_1, I_1 \ldots I_{u-1}I_v \ldots I_{t+1})$ exists. Then

$$\delta_T(q_1, I_1 \ldots I_{u-1}I_v \ldots I_{t+1}) = \delta_T(q_u, I_v \ldots I_{t+1})$$
$$= \delta_T(q_v, I_v \ldots I_{t+1})$$
$$= \delta_T(q_1, J).$$

Thus (ii) in the notation of $(p_1; q_1; t+1)$ holds. Hence $(p_1; q_1; t+1)$ holds.

(b) Let m and n be positive integers. Let S and T be the machines in Figs. 2.18 and 2.19, respectively. Consider the tape

$$J = I_1 \ldots I_{nm},$$

where

$$I_{nj+i} = I^1 \quad \text{for} \quad j = 0, \ldots, m-1 \quad \text{and} \quad 1 \le i < n,$$

and

$$I_{jn+n} = I^2.$$

It is easily seen that $\lambda(p_1, J) \ne \lambda(q_1, J)$. However $(p_1; q_1; nm-1)$ holds. Thus (b) is proved.

Again we obtain as a corollary a result which sharpens (c) of Theorem 2.1.

Corollary. Let S and T be sequential machines, with S having no output-empty states. In the notation of Lemma 2.3, $x \le y$ if and only if (x, y) is in R_{nm}, where $n = \#(K_S)$ and $m = \#(K_T)$. Furthermore, nm is the smallest possible number in the general case.

EXERCISE 12. Construct machines S and T in (b) of Theorem 2.3 for $n = 4$ and $m = 3$.

EXERCISE 13. If S is a complete machine, show that the number nm in Theorem 2.3 can be lowered to $n + m + 1$. [*Hint:* Use Theorem 1.2.]

2.3 Compatibility. The basic theory underlying a procedure toward solving the minimization problem involves the concept of compatibility of states in a machine. Two states are compatible if common applicable tapes produce common output sequences. More precisely,

Definition 2.5. Let S and T be sequential machines. State p in S is said to be *compatible* with q in T if $\lambda_S(p, J) = \lambda_T(q, J)$ for every tape J which is applicable to *both* p and q. States which are not compatible are said to be *incompatible*.

	I^1	I^2
p_1	p_2 E^1	
p_2	E^3	p_1 E^2
p_3		p_2 E^2

FIGURE 2.20

	I^1	I^2	I^3
q_1	E^2		q_3 E^1
q_2	E^1	E^2	q_2 E^3
q_3	q_2 E^3	E^2	

FIGURE 2.21

Note that tapes which are applicable to one of the states but not the other are of no concern in the determination of compatibility.

From Definition 2.5, it follows that if p is (in)compatible with q, then q is (in)compatible with p. This is also expressed as p and q being (in)compatible.

EXAMPLE 1. Let S and T be the machines in Figs. 2.20 and 2.21, respectively. The set of compatible pairs (p, q) of states p in S and q in T is

$$\{(p_1, q_2), (p_2, q_3), (p_3, q_1), (p_3, q_2), (p_3, q_3)\}.$$

Observe that while q_2 and p_3, and p_3 and q_1 are compatible pairs, q_2 and q_1 are incompatible. Thus compatibility is not a transitive relation.

The reason compatibility is important in reduction is that if two states are compatible, then it may be possible to find one state with the terminal characteristics of both. If two states are incompatible, then no one state has the terminal characteristics of both.

There is a sequence of results, Theorems 2.4 through 2.7 below, yielding a finite procedure for determining all pairs (x, y) of compatible states x and y. The proofs are left as exercises.

Theorem 2.4. Let S and T be sequential machines with n and m states, respectively. If states p_1 in S and q_1 in T are such that $\lambda_S(p_1, J) = \lambda_T(q_1, J)$ for each tape J, of length $k \leq nm$, which is applicable to both p_1 and q_1, then p_1 is compatible with q_1. The number nm is the smallest possible bound in the general case.

Theorem 2.5. Let p_1 and q_1 be states in a sequential machine S having n states. If $\lambda(p_1, J) = \lambda(q_1, J)$ for each tape J, of length

$$k \leq \frac{n(n-1)}{2},$$

which is applicable to both p_1 and q_1, then p_1 and q_1 are compatible

	I^1		I^2	
p_1	p_2	1		
p_2		1	p_3	2
p_3	p_2	1		2
p_4	p_4	2	p_2	

FIGURE 2.22

states. The number $n(n - 1)/2$ is the smallest possible number in the general case.

Theorem 2.6. Let S and T be sequential machines. Let $n = \#(K_{S_*})$ and $m = \#(K_{T_*})$, where S_* and T_* are defined by the notation preceding Theorem 2.1. Denote by Q_1 the set of ordered pairs (x, y) of states x in S_* and y in T_* such that $\lambda_S(x, I) = \lambda_T(y, I)$ for each input applicable to both x and y. In general, let Q_{k+1} be the set of all pairs (x, y) in Q_k such that $\big(\delta_S(x, I), \delta_T(y, I)\big)$ is in Q_k for each input I applicable to both x and y for which $\delta_S(x, I)$ and $\delta_T(y, I)$ exist. Then states x in S and y in T are compatible if and only if x is output-empty, y is output-empty, or (x, y) is in Q_{nm}. Furthermore, if $Q_k = Q_{k+1}$ for some integer k, then $Q_k = Q_{nm}$.

Theorem 2.7. Let S be a sequential machine. Let $n = \#(K_{S_*})$, where S_* is defined by the notation preceding Theorem 2.1. Denote by Q_1 the set of all unordered pairs (x, y) of states in S_* such that $\lambda(x, I) = \lambda(y, I)$ for each input I applicable to both x and y. In general, let Q_{k+1} be the set of all pairs (x, y) in Q_k such that $\big(\delta(x, I), \delta(y, I)\big)$ is in Q_k for each input I applicable to both x and y for which $\delta(x, I)$ and $\delta(y, I)$ exist. Then x and y are compatible states in S if and only if x is output-empty, y is output-empty, or (x, y) is in $Q_{n(n-1)/2}$. Furthermore, if $Q_k = Q_{k+1}$ for some integer k, then $Q_k = Q_{n(n-1)/2}$.

EXAMPLE 2. Let S be the machine in Fig. 2.22. Then $S_* = S$,

$$Q_1 = Q \cup \{(p_1, p_2), (p_1, p_3), (p_2, p_3)\},$$

$$\text{where } Q = \{(p_i, p_i) | 1 \leq i \leq 4\},$$

and

$$Q_2 = Q_1.$$

Thus Q_2 is the set of all compatible pairs (x, y) of states in S.

	I^1	I^2	I^3
p_1	p_2 1		p_3 2
p_2		p_4 2	
p_3	p_7 2		p_6 1
p_4		p_2 1	
p_5	p_5 1		p_3 2
p_6		p_1 2	p_7 1
p_7	p_6 2		p_1 2
p_8		p_4 2	p_2 1

FIGURE 2.23

	I^1	I^2	I^3
p_1	1		
p_2	p_5 2	p_6 2	
p_3	p_5 1		p_6 3
p_4		p_3 1	p_3 2
p_5	p_3	p_7	p_2
p_6	p_2 2		1
p_7	p_3 2	p_1 1	2

FIGURE 2.24

	I^1	I^2
p_1	p_2 E^1	
p_2	E^1	E^2
p_3	p_2	p_1
p_4	p_4 E^1	E^1

FIGURE 2.25

	I^1	I^2	I^3
q_1	q_2 E^1		
q_2	q_5 E^1	E^2	E^1
q_3		q_1 E^1	q_1 E^2
q_4	q_3		q_1
q_5	q_3 E^1	q_2 E^1	q_4 E^1

FIGURE 2.26

EXERCISE 1. Find the set of all compatible pairs (x, y) of states in the machine given in (a) Fig. 2.23, (b) Fig. 2.24.

EXERCISE 2. Let S and T be the machines in Figs. 2.25 and 2.26, respectively. Find the set of all compatible pairs (x, y) of states x in S and y in T.

EXERCISE 3. Prove Theorem 2.4.

EXERCISE 4. Prove Theorem 2.5.

EXERCISE 5. Prove Theorem 2.6.

EXERCISE 6. Prove Theorem 2.7.

EXERCISE 7. Let S and T be input-independent machines. [A sequential machine is said to be *input-independent* if for each state p, $\lambda(p, I) = \lambda(p, J)$ for all inputs I and J applicable to p.] Let $m = \#(K_S)$ and $n = \#(K_T)$, with $m \leq n$. Show that p in S and q in T are compatible states if and only if $\lambda_S(p, J) = \lambda_T(q, J)$ for every tape J of length $\leq m(n - 1) + 1$. Also show that this is the smallest possible bound in the general case.

EXERCISE 8. Let S be an input-independent machine with n states. Show that states p and q in S are compatible if and only if $\lambda(p, J) = \lambda(q, J)$ for every tape J, applicable to both p and q, of length $\leq (n^2 - 2n)/4 + 1$ if n is even and $\leq (n^2 - 2n + 1)/4 + 1$ if n is odd. Also show that these numbers are the smallest possible in the general case.

2.4 Reduction. We now present a procedure for finding a solution to the minimization problem. Part of the procedure is mechanical and part is trial-and-error.

Lemma 2.5. Let S and T be sequential machines. Let * be a relation between the states of S and those of T satisfying the following three conditions:

(i) If $x * y$ holds, then $\lambda_S(x, I) = \lambda_T(y, I)$ for each input I applicable to x.

(ii) If $x * y$ holds and if $\delta_S(x, I)$ exists for an input applicable to x, then $\delta_T(y, I)$ exists and $\delta_S(x, I) * \delta_T(y, I)$ holds.

(iii) To each state x in S there is at least one state y in T for which $x * y$ holds.

Then $x \leq y$ if $x * y$ holds; and $S \leq T$.[†]

Proof. We shall use Lemma 2.3. Suppose that $x * y$ holds. By (i) and (ii) of the hypothesis, (x, y) is in R_1. Continuing by induction, assume that (x, y) is in R_k whenever $x * y$ holds. Let $x * y$ hold. Then (x, y) is in R_k. If the input I is applicable to x, then $\delta_S(x, I) * \delta_T(y, I)$ holds by (ii), so that $(\delta_S(x, I), \delta_T(y, I))$ is in R_k by the induction hypothesis. Thus (x, y) is in R_{k+1}. It follows from (a) of Lemma 2.3 that $x \leq y$ if $x * y$ holds.

For each state x in S by (iii) there is a y in T so that $x * y$ holds; thus $x \leq y$. Therefore $S \leq T$.

Several preliminary concepts are needed in order to understand Theorem 2.8. These are now presented.

[†] Compare with Lemma 1.3.

Definition 2.6. Let S be a sequential machine. A family $H = \{A_\alpha | \alpha\}$ of nonempty subsets of K_S is said to be a *closed* family of S if the following three conditions are satisfied.

(1) The states in each A_α are pairwise compatible.

(2) $\cup_\alpha A_\alpha = K_S$.

(3) For each input I and each A_α in H, the set

$$\delta^*(A_\alpha, I) = \{\delta(q, I) | q \text{ in } A_\alpha, \lambda(q, I) \text{ exists}\}$$

is a (possibly empty) subset of some A_β in H.

EXAMPLE 1. For the sequential machine in Fig. 2.27, let

$$A_1 = \{p_1, p_2, p_3\},$$

$$A_2 = \{p_4, p_5, p_6\},$$

and

$$H = \{A_1, A_2\}.$$

H satisfies (1) and (2) in Definition 2.6. Since $\lambda(p_2, I^1)$ does not exist,

$$\delta^*(A_1, I^1) = \{\delta(p_1, I^1), \delta(p_3, I^1)\}$$

$$= \{p_4, p_5\} \subseteq A_2.$$

	I^1		I^2
p_1	p_4	E^1	E^2
p_2	p_2		E^2
p_3	p_5	E^1	E^2
p_4			E^1
p_5	p_4		E^1
p_6		E^2	E^1

FIGURE 2.27

Thus (3) is also satisfied. Therefore H is a closed family.

EXERCISE 1. Let S be the sequential machine in Fig. 2.27. Which of the following families is closed?

(i) $H = \{A_1, A_2\}$,

where

$$A_1 = \{p_1, p_3, p_5\} \quad \text{and} \quad A_2 = \{p_2, p_4, p_6\}.$$

(ii) $H = \{A_1, A_2, A_3\}$,

where

$$A_1 = \{p_1, p_2\}, \quad A_2 = \{p_2, p_3\}, \quad \text{and} \quad A_3 = \{p_4, p_5, p_6\}.$$

(iii) $H = \{A_1, A_2, A_3, A_4\}$,

where

$$A_1 = \{p_1, p_3\}, \quad A_2 = \{p_4, p_5\},$$

$$A_3 = \{p_4, p_6\}, \quad A_4 = \{p_2\}.$$

	I^1	I^2
q_1	E^1	q_2
q_2		q_1 E^2

FIGURE 2.28

	I^1	I^2	I^3
q_1	E^1	q_2	q_3
q_2	q_3 E^3	q_1 E^2	E^1
q_3		E^2	q_2

FIGURE 2.29

EXERCISE 2. Call a set A of states of a machine *maximal compatible* if (i) all states in A are pairwise compatible, and (ii) the addition of any other state to A destroys the property in (i). Show that the family H of maximal compatible sets is a closed family of S.

Lemma 2.6. A family $H = \{A_a|\alpha\}$ of nonempty sets of states of a sequential machine S is closed if and only if

(i)   it satisfies (2) and (3) in Definition 2.6, and

(ii) for each A_α in H and all states q_1 and q_2 in A_α, $\lambda(q_1, I) = \lambda(q_2, I)$ for each input I applicable to both q_1 and q_2.

The proof is left as an exercise.

Definition 2.7. The sequential machines S and T are said to be *isomorphic* if $\Sigma_S = \Sigma_T$, and there exists a one-to-one mapping f of K_S onto K_T such that for each element p in K_S and each I in Σ_S the following two conditions hold:

(i) $\delta_S(p, I)$ exists if and only if $\delta_T(f(p), I)$ exists; and if either exists, then $\delta_T[f(p), I] = f[\delta_S(p, I)]$.

(ii) $\lambda_S(p, I)$ exists if and only if $\lambda_T[f(p), I]$ exists; and if either exists, then $\lambda_S(p, I) = \lambda_T[f(p), I]$.

Two machines are isomorphic if in their δ, λ matrices, the states of one are a relabeling of the states of the other.

Definition 2.8. The sequential machine T is said to be an *extension* of the sequential machine S if $\Sigma_S \subseteq \Sigma_T$, $K_S \subseteq K_T$, $\delta_T(q, I) = \delta_S(q, I)$ whenever $\delta_S(q, I)$ exists, and $\lambda_T(q, I) = \lambda_S(q, I)$ whenever $\lambda_S(q, I)$ exists.

EXAMPLE 2. The machine in Fig. 2.29 is an extension of the machine in Fig. 2.28.

Theorem 2.8. Let S be a sequential machine with no output-empty states.

(a) Let T be any sequential machine such that $S \leq T$. For each state p in T let $A(p) = \{q | q$ in $S,\ q \leq p\}$. Let H be the family of those $A(p)$ which are nonempty. Then H is a closed family of S.

(b) Let $H = \{A_\alpha | \alpha\}$ be a closed family of S. For each A_α in H and each I in Σ, if $\delta^*(A_\alpha, I)$ is nonempty, let $A(\alpha, I)$ be an element of H for which $\delta^*(A_\alpha, I) \subseteq A(\alpha, I)$. Then there exists a sequential machine $T = (H, \Sigma_S, \Delta_S, \delta_T, \lambda_T)$ with the following properties. For each A_α in H and each I in Σ, (i) $\delta_T(A_\alpha, I)$ exists if and only if $\delta^*(A_\alpha, I)$ is nonempty, in which case $\delta_T(A_\alpha, I) = A(\alpha, I)$; (ii) $\lambda_T(A_\alpha, I)$ exists if and only if there is an element q in A_α to which I is applicable, in which case $\lambda_T(A_\alpha, I) = \lambda_S(q, I)$; (iii) $S \leq T$, with $q \leq A_\alpha$ if q is an element of A_α.

(c) Let W be a minimal-state machine of S and let $H = \{A(p) | p$ in $W\}$ be the closed family of S generated by W. There exists a sequential machine T satisfying (b) and such that W is isomorphic to an extension of T under the mapping f which takes an element p in K_W into $A(p)$ in K_T.

Proof. (a) Since $S \leq T$, for each state q in S there is a state p in T so that $q \leq p$. Thus $K_S \subseteq \cup A(p)$. Since $\cup A(p) \subseteq K_S$ by definition of the $A(p)$, $K_S = \cup A(p)$. Thus (2) in Definition 2.6 is satisfied.

Let q_1 and q_2 be states in any $A(p)$. By definition, $q_1 \leq p$ and $q_2 \leq p$. For each tape J applicable to both q_1 and q_2, $\lambda(q_1, J) = \lambda(p, J)$ and $\lambda(q_2, J) = \lambda(p, J)$, whence $\lambda(q_1, J) = \lambda(q_2, J)$. Then q_1 and q_2 are compatible. Thus (1) in Definition 2.6 is satisfied.

Let $A(p)$ in H and I in Σ be given. Now let q be any state in $A(p)$ for which $\delta(q, I)$ and $\lambda(q, I)$ exist. Since $\delta(q, I)$ is not output-empty, there exists an input I_1 applicable to $\delta(q, I)$. Then II_1 is applicable to q. Since $q \leq p$, then $\lambda(p, II_1)$ exists. Thus $\delta(p, I)$ exists. By Lemma 2.1, $\delta(q, I) \leq \delta(p, I)$. Then

$$\delta^*(A(p), I) = \{\delta(q, I) | q \text{ in } A(p),\ \lambda(q, I) \text{ exists}\}$$

is a subset of $A[\delta(p, I)]$. Thus (3) in Definition 2.6 is satisfied.

Since (1), (2), and (3) hold, H is a closed family of S.

(b) Let $K_T = H, \Sigma_T = \Sigma_S$, and $\Delta_T = \Delta_S$. Define δ_T so as to satisfy (i). Let I be an element in Σ_T and A_α in H. If I is applicable to some element q in A_α, define $\lambda_T(A_\alpha, I)$ to be $\lambda_S(q, I)$. Otherwise let $\lambda_T(A_\alpha, I)$ be undefined. Since all states in A_α are compatible, the definition of λ_T is unique. Clearly T satisfies (i) and (ii). Denote by $*$ the relation between K_S and

K_T defined by $q * A_\alpha$ if and only if q is in A_α. By Lemma 2.5, $q \leq A_\alpha$ if $q * A_\alpha$ holds, and $S \leq T$; hence (b) is proved.

(c) Let W be a minimal-state machine of S. For each state p in W let $A(p) = \{q | q \leq p, q$ in $S\}$. Let H be the family of all nonempty $A(p)$. Thus $\#(H) \leq \#(K_W)$. By (a), H is a closed family of S. Let $A(p)$ in H and I in Σ_S be such that $\delta_S^*[A(p), I]$ is nonempty. Let q be any state in $A(p)$ such that $\lambda_S(q, I)$ and $\delta_S(q, I)$ both exist. Since S has no output-empty states, there exists I_1 in Σ_S which is applicable to $\delta_S(q, I)$. Then II_1 is applicable to q. Since $q \leq p$, then II_1 is applicable to p. Thus $\delta_W(p, I)$ exists. By Lemma 2.1, $\delta_S(q, I) \leq \delta_W(p, I)$. Therefore

$$\delta_S^*[A(p), I] \subseteq A[\delta_W(p, I)].$$

Denote by $A(p, I)$ the set $A[\delta_W(p, I)]$. Let T be the machine satisfying (b) for each of the $A(p, I)$ so selected. By (b), $S \leq T$.

To show that W is isomorphic to an extension of T, it is sufficient to prove that W is an extension of a machine U which is isomorphic to T. This is now done. Since W is minimal with respect to S, $\#(K_W) \leq \#(K_T) = \#(H)$. As the reverse inequality has already been shown, $\#(K_W) = \#(H)$. Thus the transformation of p into $A(p)$ is a one-to-one mapping f of $H = K_T$ onto K_W. Let U be the machine $(K_W, \Sigma_T, \Delta_T, \delta_U, \lambda_U)$, where (i) $\delta_U(p, I)$ exists if and only if $\delta_T(A(p), I)$ exists, in which case $\delta_U(p, I) = \delta_W(p, I)$, and (ii) $\lambda_U(p, I)$ exists if and only if $\lambda_T[A(p), I]$ exists, in which case $\lambda_U(p, I) = \lambda_T[A(p), I]$. It is readily verified that U is isomorphic to T and W is an extension of U.

The essence of the above theorem is that for each machine S with no output-empty states, (i) the set of states in any minimal-state machine of S may be considered a closed family of S, and (ii) all minimal-state machines of S are extensions of closed families of S as defined in (b).

Suppose that S has output-empty states and S_* is defined as in the notation preceding Theorem 2.1. By exercise 8, Section 2.2, $S \leq S_*$ and $S_* \leq S$. Thus T is a minimal-state machine of S if and only if T is a minimal-state machine of S_*. As S_* has no output-empty states, Theorem 2.8 may be applied to S_*.

Suppose that H is a closed family of a machine S with no output-empty states. If there exist two elements of H such that $A_1 \subseteq A_2$, then, as is easily seen, $H - \{A_1\}$ is also a closed family. Thus we obtain

Corollary 1. Let S be a sequential machine with no output-empty states. If H is a closed family of S with two elements A_1 and A_2 such that $A_1 \subseteq A_2$, then H cannot be the set of states of a minimal-state machine of S whose next-state function and output function are defined by (b).

	I^1	I^2
p_1	p_2 E^1	
p_2	p_1 E^2	
p_3	p_4 E^1	
p_4	p_5 E^2	p_5 E^1
p_5	p_6 E^1	
p_6	p_3 E^2	p_3 E^2
p_7	p_6	p_1

FIGURE 2.30

	I^1	I^2
p_1	p_2 E^1	
p_2	p_1 E^2	
p_3	p_4 E^1	
p_4	p_5 E^2	p_5 E^1
p_5	p_6 E^1	
p_6	p_3 E^2	p_3 E^2

FIGURE 2.31

From (a) of Theorem 2.8 and Corollary 1 there follows

Corollary 2. Let S be a sequential machine S having no output-empty states. Then no minimal-state machine of S can contain two states p and q such that $p \leq q$.

Corollary 2 is easily seen to be true even if S has output-empty states. Theorem 2.8 and the subsequent discussion suggest the following procedure for finding a minimal-state machine T of S. (1) Construct S_*. (2) Determine a closed family H of S_* such that $\#(H) \leq \#(G)$ for every closed family G of S_*. (3) Construct T as in (b).

At present there is no known method of executing step (2) except by judicious trial-and-error.

Unsolved problem. Find an "efficient" method of executing step (2).

EXAMPLE 3. Let S be the machine in Fig. 2.30. Machine S_* appears in Fig. 2.31. The set of compatible pairs is

$$\{(p_1, p_3), (p_1, p_5), (p_2, p_4), (p_2, p_6)\} \cup \{(p_i, p_i) | 1 \leq i \leq 6\}.$$

The family of maximal compatible sets is

$$\{\langle p_1, p_3 \rangle, \langle p_1, p_5 \rangle, \langle p_2, p_4 \rangle, \langle p_2, p_6 \rangle\}.$$

Let H be a closed family, to be calculated, which yields a minimal state machine T. Since the family of maximal compatible sets is closed, $\#(H) \leq 4$. Suppose $\#(H) < 4$. Since p_1, p_4, and p_6 are pairwise incompatible, each is in a different element of H. Then $\#(H) \geq 3$. Thus $\#(H) = 3$. Let

	I^1	I^2
A_1	A_3 E^1	
A_2	A_4 E^1	
A_3	A_2 E^2	A_2 E^1
A_4	A_1 E^2	A_1 E^2

FIGURE 2.32

	I^1		I^2	
p_1	p_2		p_3	0
p_2	p_3	0	p_5	0
p_3	p_4	0	p_6	
p_4	p_5	1	p_3	0
p_5			p_6	0
p_6	p_2			1

FIGURE 2.33

$H = \{A_1, A_2, A_3\}$, with p_1 in A_1, p_4 in A_2, and p_6 in A_3. Since p_3 is incompatible with p_4 and p_6, p_3 must also be in A_1. As p_5 is incompatible with p_3, p_4, and p_6, p_5 is not in A_1, A_2, or A_3. Thus $\cup A_i \neq K_{S_*}$. Therefore $\{A_1, A_2, A_3\}$ is not a closed family. Hence $\#(H) = 4$. The minimal-state machine of S constructed from H by (b) of Theorem 2.8 is given in Fig. 2.32, where

$$A_1 = \langle p_1, p_3 \rangle,$$

$$A_2 = \langle p_1, p_5 \rangle,$$

$$A_3 = \langle p_2, p_4 \rangle,$$

and

$$A_4 = \langle p_2, p_6 \rangle.$$

EXAMPLE 4. Let S be the machine in Fig. 2.33. Then $S_* = S$. The set of compatible pairs is

$$\{(p_1, p_2), (p_1, p_3), (p_1, p_4), (p_1, p_5), (p_3, p_5), (p_3, p_6), (p_4, p_5)\} \cup Q,$$

where $Q = \{(p_i, p_i) | 1 \leq i \leq 6\}$. The family of maximal compatible sets is

$$\{\langle p_1, p_2 \rangle, \langle p_1, p_3, p_5 \rangle, \langle p_1, p_4, p_5 \rangle, \langle p_3, p_6 \rangle\}.$$

Let H be a closed family, to be calculated, which yields a minimal-state machine T. Since there are four maximal compatible sets, $\#(H) \leq 4$. As p_2, p_3, and p_4 are pairwise incompatible, each is in a different element of H. Thus $\#(H) \geq 3$. Suppose $\#(H) = 3$. Then $H = \{A_1, A_2, A_3\}$, with p_2 in A_1, p_3 in A_2, and p_4 in A_3. Since p_6 is incompatible with p_2 and p_4, p_6 must be in A_2. Since p_5 is incompatible with p_2 and p_6, p_5 must be in A_3. Since p_1 is incompatible with p_6, p_1 must be in A_1 or A_3.

	I^1	I^2
A_1	A_2 0	A_3 0
A_2	A_3 0	1
A_3	A_3 1	A_2 0

FIGURE 2.34

	I^1	I^2
p_1	p_4 0	
p_2	p_4 0	p_3 1
p_3		p_4
p_4	p_2 1	1

FIGURE 2.35

	I^1	I^2
p_1	p_3 0	p_6 1
p_2	p_3 0	p_5
p_3	p_2	p_3 0
p_4	p_2 0	p_3
p_5	p_4	p_6
p_6		p_6 0

FIGURE 2.36

If we let p_1 be in A_3, then we obtain a closed family H. The machine T constructed from H is given in Fig. 2.34. If we let p_1 be in A_1, then this would imply that $\delta^*(A_1, I^2) = \{p_3, p_5\}$ is a subset of some A_i. It cannot be A_1, since p_2 and p_5 are incompatible states. It cannot be A_2, since p_5 and p_6 are incompatible. It cannot be A_3, since p_3 and p_4 are incompatible. Thus the machine in Fig. 2.34 is, essentially, the only minimal-state machine of S.

Additional details and examples of the reduction process are found in reference [P1].

EXERCISE 3. Find a minimal-state machine of the machine in (a) Fig. 2.35, (b) Fig. 2.36, (c) Fig. 2.37.

EXERCISE 4. Let S be a strongly connected machine. [S is said to be *strongly connected* if for each ordered pair (p, q) of states p and q in S there is a tape J applicable to p so that $\delta(p, J) = q$.] Prove that any minimal-state machine of S is strongly connected.

EXERCISE 5. Let S be the direct sum of strongly connected machines. [S is said to be the *direct sum* of the machines $S_1, \ldots, S_r$ if the states in S_i are different from those in S_j, $i \neq j$, and if the δ, λ matrix of S is obtained by placing the δ, λ matrix of each S_i, $i \geq 2$, under the δ, λ

	I^1		I^2		I^3	
p_1	p_1	1	p_2	1		
p_2	p_2	2	p_1	1		
p_3			p_4	1	p_3	1
p_4			p_5	1	p_4	2
p_5			p_3	1	p_5	3
p_6	p_5	2			p_2	3
p_7	p_4	1			p_1	2

FIGURE 2.37

matrix of S_{i-1}.] Let T be any minimal-state machine of S. Show that there exists a minimal-state machine $U = (K_T, \Sigma_T, \Delta_T, \delta_U, \lambda_U)$ of S, where $\delta_U(q, I) = \delta_T(q, I)$ whenever $\delta_U(q, I)$ exists, and $\lambda_U(q, I) = \lambda_T(q, I)$ whenever $\lambda_U(q, I)$ exists, which is the direct sum of strongly connected machines.

EXERCISE 6. Let S be a machine satisfying the following condition: For each state p in S and each input I applicable to p, II is applicable to p, $\lambda(p, II) = EE$, and $\delta(p, II) = \delta(p, I)$. Show that there exists a minimal-state machine of S which also satisfies this condition.

2.5 Synthesis. Until now we have dealt with the study of relationships between the various entities comprising a sequential machine. This aspect is called analysis. In this section we consider the construction of a machine which satisfies a given set of specifications. This aspect is called synthesis. In particular, we shall treat the problem of finding a machine, with the fewest number of states possible, which satisfies a prescribed set of "terminal characteristics."

The obvious course of procedure in constructing a machine which is minimal state with respect to a set of terminal characteristics, is to (i) construct a machine S satisfying the specifications, and (ii) find a minimal-state machine $T(S)$ of S. However, there are several pitfalls associated with (i) and (ii). For example, how does one enact (i)? If S satisfies the specifications, why must $T(S)$ also satisfy the specifications? And if S_1 and S_2 are machines satisfying (i), with $T(S_1)$ and $T(S_2)$ minimal-state machines of S_1 and S_2, respectively, it might very well be that $\#[K_{T(S_1)}] \neq \#[K_{T(S_2)}]$. Thus the number of states in a machine obtained by (i) and (ii) might depend on the S selected by (i). In summary, indiscriminate use of (i) and (ii) may not lead to the desired result.

We now make a basic assumption. It will be assumed that the specifications are in such a form as to be satisfied by a machine U *if and only if there exists a finite number of states in U having a prescribed input-output behavior*, i.e., if and only if there exists a finite number of states q in U such that the application of specified input sequences (depending on q) to the machine initially at q produces specified output sequences. A synthesis technique is now described in two stages.

The first stage consists of constructing a machine S as follows. For each distinct input-output behavior demanded by the specifications, assign a state, designated by the symbol q, to yield exactly this input-output behavior. Let $A(q, I)$ be the following set of input-output sequences. An input-output sequence $J_1 - J_2$ is in $A(q, I)$ if and only if for some output E, $IJ_1 - EJ_2$ is associated with q. Let $\delta(q, I)$ be a state which is assigned to yield the input-output behavior consisting of precisely the input-output sequences in $A(q, I)$. The machine S, consisting of all the states q together with the δ- and λ-functions, satisfies the prescribed input-output behavior and thus the specifications.

The most important property that S possesses is that for any sequential machine T, $S \leq T$ *if and only if* T satisfies the specifications. To see this, first suppose that $S \leq T$. For each input-output behavior demanded by the synthesis conditions, there exists a state q in S satisfying it. Since $S \leq T$, there exists a state p in T so that $q \leq p$. Then p, and thus T, satisfies this input-output behavior. Therefore T contains a finite number of states which satisfy the specified input-output behavior. By the basic assumption about the specifications, T satisfies the synthesis conditions. Now suppose that T is any machine satisfying the synthesis conditions. Let q be any state of S. From the way S is defined, the input-output behavior of q is exactly the input-output sequences demanded by the specifications for some state. Since T satisfies the specifications, there is a state p in T which produces these input-output sequences (and perhaps others). Hence $q \leq p$. Thus $S \leq T$.

The second stage of the synthesis procedure is to find a minimal-state machine, call it W, of S. This is done by the method indicated in Section 2.4.

Consider the machine W obtained from stage two. Since $S \leq W$, W satisfies the specifications. Suppose that T is any machine satisfying the synthesis conditions. Then, as noted above, $S \leq T$. Since W is a minimal-state machine of S, $\#(K_W) \leq \#(K_T)$. Thus W is a machine, with the fewest states possible, which satisfies the original specifications.

As an illustration of the general synthesis procedure, suppose that the specifications are given explicitly in the form of a finite number of input-output sequences, each either of finite length or ultimately periodic. The input-output sequences of finite length are as follows.

$$\text{Input sequence:} \quad I_1^i \dots I_{n(i)}^i$$
$$1 \leq i \leq r.$$
$$\text{Output sequence:} \quad E_1^i \dots E_{n(i)}^i$$

The ultimately periodic input-output sequences are as follows.

$$\text{Input sequence:} \quad I_1^i \dots I_{k(i)}^i \overbrace{I_{k(i)+1}^i \dots I_{n(i)}^i}^{\text{periodic}}$$
$$r + 1 \leq i \leq s.$$
$$\text{Output sequence:} \quad E_1^i \dots E_{k(i)}^i \underbrace{E_{k(i)+1}^i \dots E_{n(i)}^i}_{\text{periodic}}$$

In accordance with the synthesis procedure, associate states with the input-output behavior as follows.

$$I_1^i \dots I_{n(i)}^i$$
$$q_1^i \dots q_{n(i)}^i \qquad 1 \leq i \leq s.$$
$$E_1^i \dots E_{n(i)}^i$$

Define the functions λ and δ thus. Let $\lambda(q_j^i, I_j^i) = E_j^i$ for $1 \leq i \leq s$ and $1 \leq j \leq n(i)$. Let $\delta(q_j^i, I_j^i) = q_{j+1}^i$ for $1 \leq i \leq s$ and $j < n(i)$. Let $\delta(q_{n(i)}^i, I_{n(i)}^i) = q_{k(i)+1}^i$ for $r + 1 \leq i \leq s$. The states q_j^i, the inputs I_j^i, the outputs E_j^i, and the two functions δ and λ form a machine S. Then a minimal-state machine W of S is a machine, with the fewest number of states possible, which satisfies the synthesis input-output sequences.

EXAMPLE 1. Consider the input-output sequences given by

$$I^1 I^2 \qquad\qquad \overbrace{I^1 I^1 I^2 I^1}^{\text{periodic}}$$
$$\text{and}$$
$$0 \; 0 \qquad\qquad \underbrace{1 \; 0 \; 1 \; 0}_{\text{periodic}}$$

The assignment of states yields

$$I^1 I^2 \qquad\qquad \overbrace{I^1 I^1 I^2 I^1}^{\text{periodic}}$$
$$q_1^1 q_2^1 \quad \text{and} \quad q_1^2 q_2^1 q_3^2 q_4^2$$
$$0 \; 0 \qquad\qquad \underbrace{1 \; 0 \; 1 \; 0}_{\text{periodic}}$$

	I^1	I^2
q_1^1	q_2^1 0	
q_2^1		0
q_1^2	q_2^2 1	
q_2^2	q_3^2 0	
q_3^2		q_4^2 1
q_4^2	q_2^1 0	

FIGURE 2.38

	I^1	I^2
A_1	A_2 0	0
A_2	A_3 0	0
A_3	A_2 1	A_1 1

FIGURE 2.39

Machine S is given in Fig. 2.38. A minimal-state machine W of S is given in Fig. 2.39. There $A_1 = \langle q_1^1, q_2^1, q_4^2 \rangle$, $A_2 = \langle q_2^1, q_2^2 \rangle$, and $A_3 = \langle q_1^2, q_3^2 \rangle$.

EXERCISE 1. Find a machine, with the fewest number of states possible, which satisfies the following input-output sequences.

$$aba$$
$$001$$

periodic
$$\overbrace{abbaa}$$
$$10001$$
periodic

periodic
$$\overbrace{ba}$$
$$00$$
periodic

As another illustration of the synthesis procedure let I_t denote the present input, E_t the present output, I_{t-i} the ith previous input, and E_{t-i} the ith previous output. Suppose that the specifications are partly expressible in the form

$$(*) \quad E_t = f(I_{t-r}, \ldots, I_t, E_{t-s}, \ldots, E_{t-1}),$$

i.e., the present output depends only on the present input, the r previous inputs, and the s previous outputs. In general, the specifications have additional provisions. Two classes of specifications which incorporate $(*)$ to some extent are given in (A) and (B) below.

Condition (A). The machine is to have a start state q_1. Furthermore, there exist non-negative integers r and s and certain tapes $I_1 \ldots I_m$ which are applicable to q_1 such that

(1) $E_t = f(I_1, \ldots, I_t)$ for $t \leq \max \{r, s\}$, where $\max \{r, s\}$ is the larger of r and s.

(2) $E_t = f(I_{t-r}, \ldots, I_t, E_{t-s}, \ldots, E_{t-1})$ for $t > \max \{r, s\}$, for certain tapes $I_{t-r} \ldots I_t$, and for certain output sequences $E_{t-s} \ldots E_{t-1}$ (depending on $I_{t-r} \ldots I_{t-1}$).

(3) The tapes $I_1 \ldots I_m$ not covered by either (1) or (2) are don't-care tapes, that is, are of no concern.

The general synthesis technique described earlier is valid for specifications satisfying (A). Suppose the specifications satisfy (A). In view of (1), if $t \leq \max \{r, s\}$, then E_t depends on $I_1, \ldots, I_t$. If $t > \max \{r, s\}$, then E_t depends on $I_{t-r}, \ldots, I_t, E_{t-s}, \ldots, E_{t-1}$ (thus E_t actually depends on $I_1, \ldots, I_t$). Let q_1 be the start state. For $k < \max \{r, s\}$, associate a distinct state q with each applicable tape $I_1 \ldots I_k$. For $k \geq \max \{r, s\}$, associate a distinct state q with each sequence $J = I_{k-r+1}$, $\ldots, I_k, E_{k-s+1}, \ldots, E_k$ having the property that J is a sequence in (2) for some input I_{k+1}. The synthesis technique may then be applied to construct δ and λ, and thus S. A minimal-state machine W of S is a machine, with the fewest number of states possible, which satisfies the specifications.

EXAMPLE 2. Consider the following specifications. There are four inputs I^0, I^1, I^2, and I^3, and two outputs 0 and 1. The don't-care tapes are those tapes in which at least one of the eight pairs of inputs listed below occur consecutively in the order given:

$$I^0, I^0; \qquad I^0, I^3; \qquad I^1, I^1; \qquad I^1, I^2;$$

$$I^2, I^2; \qquad I^2, I^1; \qquad I^3, I^3; \qquad I^3, I^0.$$

For all other tapes, when the machine is started at q_1, the output $E_t = 1$ is to occur if and only if $I_{t-2} = I^0$, $I_{t-1} = I^1$, $I_t = I^3$; or if $I_{t-2} = I^0$, $I_{t-1} = I^2$, and $I_t = I^3$.

Clearly the present output depends only on the present input and the two previous inputs. Letting $r = 2$ and $s = 0$, associate q_2 with I^0; q_3 with I^0, I^1; q_4 with I^0, I^2; q_5 with I^2; q_6 with I^2, I^0; q_7 with I^2, I^3; q_8 with I^1; q_9 with I^1, I^0; q_{10} with I^1, I^3; q_{11} with I^3; q_{12} with I^3, I^1; and q_{13} with I^3, I^2. The synthesis procedure yields the machine S in Fig. 2.40. For example, if S is at q_{12}, then $I_{t-2} = I^3$ and $I_{t-1} = I^1$. Since I^1, I^1 and I^1, I^2 are don't-cares, I_t is restricted to either I^0 or I^3. If $I_t = I^0$, then $\lambda(q_{12}, I_t) = 0$. This is because $E_t = 1$ if and only if either $I_{t-2} = I^0$, $I_{t-1} = I^1$, and $I_t = I^3$; or $I_{t-2} = I^0$, $I_{t-1} = I^2$, and $I_t = I^3$. Similarly $\lambda(q_{12}, I^3) = 0$. If $I_t = I^0$, then $\delta(q_{12}, I_t)$ is the state associated with $I_{t-1} = I^1$ and $I_t = I^0$, that is, with q_9. If $I_t = I^3$, then $\delta(q_{12}, I_t)$ is the state associated with $I_{t-1} = I^1$ and $I_t = I^3$, that is, with q_{10}.

	I^0		I^1		I^2		I^3	
q_1	q_2	0	q_8	0	q_5	0	q_{11}	0
q_2			q_3	0	q_4	0		
q_3	q_9	0					q_{10}	1
q_4	q_6	0					q_7	1
q_5	q_6	0					q_7	0
q_6			q_3	0	q_4	0		
q_7			q_{12}	0	q_{13}	0		
q_8	q_9	0					q_{10}	0
q_9			q_3	0	q_4	0		
q_{10}			q_{12}	0	q_{13}	0		
q_{11}			q_{12}	0	q_{13}	0		
q_{12}	q_9	0					q_{10}	0
q_{13}	q_6	0					q_7	0

FIGURE 2.40

	I^0		I^1		I^2		I^3	
A_1	A_2	0	A_1	0	A_1	0	A_1	0
A_2	A_2	0	A_2	0	A_2	0	A_1	1

FIGURE 2.41

A minimal-state machine W of S is given in Fig. 2.41, with

$$A_1 = \langle q_1, q_5, q_7, q_8, q_{10}, q_{11}, q_{12}, q_{13} \rangle$$

and

$$A_2 = \langle q_2, q_3, q_4, q_6, q_9 \rangle.$$

EXAMPLE 3. Consider the following specifications. There are two inputs, 0 and 1. There also are two outputs, 0 and 1. The only tapes of interest are those where a zero always follows a one and a one always follows a zero, i.e., 0101... and 1010... . Starting at q_1 and applying a tape of interest, the first two outputs are to be 0 and 0. After the first two outputs, E_t is determined by the formula

$$E_t = I_t + E_{t-1} + E_{t-2} \pmod 2.$$

That is, $E_t = 0$ or 1 according as $I_t + E_{t-1} + E_{t-2}$ is even or odd.

At first glance it appears that E_t is a function of I_t, E_{t-2}, and E_{t-1} only. However, due to the don't-care tapes, knowledge of the previous input I_{t-1} is necessary to determine which present inputs I_t are of interest. Thus E_t also depends on I_{t-1}, so that $E_t = f(I_{t-1}, I_t, E_{t-2}, E_{t-1})$. Applying the synthesis procedure, let q_1 be the start state. Associate q_2 with the input 0 and q_3 with the input 1. Associate a distinct state with each triple $(I_{t-1}, E_{t-2}, E_{t-3})$. Thus associate q_4 with $(0, 0, 0)$, q_5 with $(1, 0, 0)$, q_6 with $(0, 0, 1)$, q_7 with $(1, 0, 1)$, q_8 with $(0, 1, 0)$, q_9 with $(1, 1, 0)$, q_{10} with $(0, 1, 1)$, and q_{11} with $(1, 1, 1)$. The synthesis procedure yields the machine in Fig. 2.42. For example, if S is at q_2, then there has been just one previous input, namely $I_1 = 0$. For $t = 2$ the specifications require E_{t-1} and E_t both to be 0. Since $I_{t-1} = 0$, then $I_t = 1$. Thus $\lambda(q_2, 1) = 0$. Also, $\delta(q_2, 1)$ is the state associated with $I_t = 1$, $E_{t-1} = 0$, and $E_t = 0$. Therefore $\delta(q_2, I) = q_5$.

A minimal-state machine W of S is in Fig. 2.43. There

$$A_1 = \langle q_1, q_2, q_6, q_8, q_9, q_{11} \rangle,$$

$$A_2 = \langle q_3, q_5, q_{10} \rangle,$$

and

$$A_3 = \langle q_4, q_7 \rangle.$$

The second class of specifications which incorporate (*) is the following.

Condition (B). For each set F_i in a given family of sets of tapes, the machine is to be started in some state $q(F_i)$. Either the resulting outputs are to satisfy (*) only after max $\{r, s\} + 1$ inputs, or the previous max $\{r, s\}$ input-outputs are assumed known and the outputs are to satisfy (*) immediately. The synthesis technique is valid when the specifications satisfy (B) (a state of S is associated with each of the different sequences of interest $I_{t-r}, \ldots, I_{t-1}, E_{t-s}, \ldots, E_{t-1}$).

EXAMPLE 4.   Consider the following specifications.   A machine is desired which satisfies condition (B). There are three inputs, I^1, I^2, and I^3. There are four outputs E^0, E^1, E^2, and E^3. The don't-care tapes are all those which contain at least one of the five pairs of inputs next listed consecutively in the order given:

$$I^1, I^1; \quad I^2, I^2; \quad I^2, I^3; \quad I^3, I^3; \quad I^3, I^2.$$

Suppose that $E_{t-1} = E^i$. Then $E_t = E^i$ if $I_t = I^1$, $E_t = E^{i+1 \ (\text{mod } 4)}$ if $I_t = I^2$, and $E_t = E^{i-1 \ (\text{mod } 4)}$ if $I_t = I^3$.

	0	1
q_1	q_2 0	q_3 0
q_2		q_5 0
q_3	q_4 0	
q_4		q_7 1
q_5	q_4 0	
q_6		q_9 0
q_7	q_{10} 1	
q_8		q_5 0
q_9	q_6 1	
q_{10}		q_{11} 1
q_{11}	q_8 0	

FIGURE 2.42

	I^1	I^2	I^3
q_1		q_6 E^1	q_{12} E^3
q_2		q_7 E^2	q_9 E^0
q_3		q_8 E^3	q_{10} E^1
q_4		q_5 E^0	q_{11} E^2
q_5	q_1 E^0		
q_6	q_2 E^1		
q_7	q_3 E^2		
q_8	q_4 E^3		
q_9	q_1 E^0		
q_{10}	q_2 E^1		
q_{11}	q_3 E^2		
q_{12}	q_4 E^3		

FIGURE 2.44

	0	1
A_1	A_1 0	A_2 0
A_2	A_3 0	A_1 1
A_3	A_2 1	A_3 1

FIGURE 2.43

	I^1	I^2	I^3
A_1	A_1 E^0	A_2 E^1	A_4 E^3
A_2	A_2 E^1	A_3 E^2	A_1 E^0
A_3	A_3 E^2	A_4 E^3	A_2 E^1
A_4	A_4 E^3	A_1 E^0	A_3 E^2

FIGURE 2.45

From the description of the specifications it is clear that E_t is a function of I_{t-1}, I_t, and E_{t-1}. Therefore associate a state with each pair (I_{t-1}, E_{t-1}). In particular, associate q_1 with (I^1, E^0), q_2 with (I^1, E^1), q_3 with (I^1, E^2), q_4 with (I^1, E^3), q_5 with (I^2, E^0), q_6 with (I^2, E^1), q_7 with (I^2, E^2), q_8 with (I^2, E^3), q_9 with (I^3, E^0), q_{10} with (I^3, E^1), q_{11} with (I^3, E^2), and q_{12} with (I^3, E^3). The machine S constructed by the synthesis procedure is given in Fig. 2.44.

A minimal-state machine W of S is in Fig. 2.45. There $A_1 = \langle q_1, q_5, q_9 \rangle$, $A_2 = \langle q_2, q_6, q_{10} \rangle$, $A_3 = \langle q_3, q_7, q_{11} \rangle$, and $A_4 = \langle q_4, q_8, q_{12} \rangle$.

EXERCISES. In 2 through 5 find a machine, with the fewest number of states possible, satisfying the given specifications.

2. There are three inputs, I^1, I^2, and I^3. There are two outputs, 0 and 1. The don't-care tapes are those containing at least one of the following three pairs of inputs listed consecutively in the order given.

$$I^1, I^1; \quad I^2, I^2; \quad \text{and} \quad I^3, I^3.$$

There is a start state q_1. $E_t = 1$ if and only if $I_t = I^3$, $I_{t-1} = I^2$, and $I_{t-2} = I^1$.

3. There are two inputs, 0 and 1. There are also two outputs, 0 and 1. The don't-care tapes are those containing two consecutive 0's. There is a start state q_1. The first two outputs are 0. For $t \geq 3$,

$$E_t = I_t + I_{t-1} + E_{t-1} + E_{t-2} \ (\text{mod } 2).$$

4. There are two inputs I^1 and I^2, and two outputs 0 and 1. There is a start state q_1. The don't-care tapes are those containing three consecutive 0's. The first two outputs are 0. For $t \geq 3$, $E_t = 1$ if and only if $I_t = 1$, $I_{t-1} = 0$, $I_{t-2} = 1$, and $E_{t-2} = 0$.

5. There are two inputs, 0 and 1. There are five outputs, $\emptyset$, A, B, C, and D. The specifications satisfy (B). $E_t = A$ if $I_{t-1} = 0$, $I_t = 0$, and $E_{t-1} = \emptyset$. $E_t = B$ if $I_{t-3} = 1$, $I_{t-2} = 0$, $I_{t-1} = 1$, $I_t = 0$, $E_{t-3} = \emptyset$, $E_{t-2} = \emptyset$, and $E_{t-1} = \emptyset$. $E_t = C$ if $I_{t-3} = 1$, $I_{t-2} = 1$, $I_{t-1} = 1$, $I_t = 0$, and $E_{t-3} = E_{t-2} = E_{t-1} = \emptyset$. $E_t = D$ if $I_{t-3} = 1$, $I_{t-2} = 0$, $I_{t-1} = I_t = 1$, and $E_{t-3} = E_{t-2} = E_{t-1} = \emptyset$. Otherwise $E_t = \emptyset$.

EXERCISE 6. Generalize exercise 5 thus. Show that the synthesis procedure is valid in the following situation. The machine is to satisfy (B). The inputs are 0 and 1. The outputs are $\emptyset$, E^1, ..., E^k. Let J_1, ..., J_k be k tapes, each J_i of length $L(i)$, with the property that for $i \neq j$ there is no tape M so that $J_i = J_j M$. [A set of such tapes is said to be a code with the *prefix* property.] $E_t = E_i$ if the previous $L(i) - 1$ inputs and I_t form J_i, and the previous $L(i) - 1$ outputs are $\emptyset$. Otherwise $E_t = \emptyset$.

EXERCISE 7. Find the equations of a (possibly incompletely defined) sequential switching circuit, with the fewest number of delay elements, having the following terminal characteristics. There are two input wires and one output wire. The don't-care input sequences are those in which any input is immediately followed by itself. The circuit is to satisfy (B). $y_1 = 0$ if and only if $(x_1^{t-3}, x_2^{t-3}) = (0, 0)$, $(x_1^{t-2}, x_2^{t-2}) = (0, 1)$, $(x_1^{t-1}, x_2^{t-1}) = (1, 0)$, and $(x_1^t, x_2^t) = (1, 1)$.

2.6 History.   Incomplete sequential machines appear in explicit form for the first time in [M2] although they are implicit in [H2]. The concept of $\leq$ is considered in [G3], as are the results in Sections 2.2 and 2.3. The concept of compatibility is due to Aufenkamp [A1]. A statement of the general reduction problem first occurs in [G3], and a general reduction procedure in [G5]. The method used in Section 2.5 is found in [P1]. Synthesis is originally treated in [H2], although slanted toward sequential switching circuits. The synthesis procedure which yields a machine with the fewest states possible is presented in [G4].

CHAPTER 3

ABSTRACT MACHINES

In a sequential machine, the set of inputs, the set of states, and the set of outputs are all finite. In addition, neither the set of inputs nor the set of outputs has any dependencies existing among its members. Two mathematical structures, quasimachines and abstract machines, which do not suffer from these restrictions, are now considered. Both quasimachines and abstract machines (i) conform to the intuitive notion of machines as devices with inputs, outputs, and states, (ii) generalize complete sequential machines, and (iii) realize a number of different situations in data processing which no other single known model does.

3.1 Basic terms. Consider a complete sequential machine

$$S = (K, \Sigma, \Delta, \delta, \lambda).$$

The set of all tapes, under the operation of concatenation, is the free semigroup W with identity generated by Σ. The set of all sequences of outputs, under the operation of concatenation, is the free semigroup Y with identity generated by Δ. The equations

$$\delta(q, J_1 J_2) = \delta[\delta(q, J_1), J_2]$$

and

$$\lambda(q, J_1 J_2) = \lambda(q, J_1)\lambda[\delta(q, J_1), J_2]$$

which hold in S are mappings from $K \times W$ into K and $K \times W$ into Δ, respectively. This suggests the following as a generalization of a complete sequential machine.

Definition 3.1. A *quasimachine* S is a 5-tuple $(K, W, Y, \delta, \lambda)$ satisfying the following axioms:

(1) K is a nonempty (not necessarily finite) set;
(2) W and Y are nonempty semigroups;
(3) δ is a mapping of $K \times W$ into K such that $\delta(q, IJ) = \delta[\delta(q, I), J]$ for each element q in K and all elements I and J in W;
(4) λ is a mapping of $K \times W$ into Y such that

$$\lambda(q, IJ) = \lambda(q, I)\lambda[\delta(q, I), J]$$

for each element q in K and all elements I and J in W.

The elements of K, W, and Y are called *states, inputs,* and *outputs,* respectively. δ is called the *next-state* function and λ the *output* function.

The main point in the generalization (other than permitting an infinite number of states) consists in allowing dependencies to exist among the inputs and outputs, respectively. This is accomplished by using a semigroup for the set of inputs and a semigroup for the set of outputs.

Let $S = (K, W, Y, \delta, \lambda)$ be a quasimachine. From axioms (3) and (4) of Definition 3.1, it follows that δ and λ are uniquely determined by their values on $K \times A$, A being any generating set of W. On the other hand, let W and Y be semigroups. Let A be a generating set of W and let K be a nonempty set. Two functions δ and λ, mapping $K \times A$ into K and Y, respectively, can always be extended to $K \times W$ by axioms (3) and (4). However, $(K, W, Y, \delta, \lambda)$ may not be a quasimachine, since δ or λ may not be *uniquely* defined on $K \times W$. For example, let W be the semigroup of three elements I^1, I^2, and I^3 with $I^i I^j = I^3$ for $1 \leq i, j \leq 3$. Let Y be the free semigroup generated by the two elements E^1 and E^2. Let $K = \{q_1\}$. Let $\delta(q_1, I^1) = \delta(q_1, I^2) = q_1$, $\lambda(q_1, I^1) = E^1$, and $\lambda(q_1, I^2) = E^2$. However, λ cannot be uniquely extended to $W \times K$, since

$$\lambda(q_1, I^1 I^2) = \lambda(q_1, I^3) = E^1 E^2,$$

whereas

$$\lambda(q_1, I^2 I^1) = \lambda(q_1, I^3) = E^2 E^1.$$

Quasimachines may be quite pathological in nature. A number of mathematical results, true for complete sequential machines, do not hold for quasimachines. These results involve concepts defined by output sequences. However, if we restrict the output semigroups to those which satisfy the left cancellation law, then, as we shall see, these results hold. The resulting quasimachines, called abstract machines, have many properties and characteristics belonging to complete sequential machines.

Definition 3.2. An *abstract machine* is a quasimachine in which the output semigroup satisfies the left cancellation law.

In contrast with a sequential machine, an abstract machine may have an infinite number of states.

An abstract machine may be considered a generalization of a complete sequential machine. Let $S = (K, \Sigma, \Delta, \delta, \lambda)$ be a complete sequential machine. Let W and Y be the free semigroups with identity generated by Σ and Δ, respectively. Consider the abstract machine $T = (K, W, Y, \delta, \lambda)$. Then S and T are identical except for the following minor logical point. In S, δ and λ are defined over $K \times \Sigma$ and then extended to $K \times W$. In T, δ and λ are defined over $K \times W$ initially.

3.2* Examples. We now present a number of examples of quasimachines and abstract machines that are relevant to data processing. In each of these examples, if W has an identity element a, then $\delta(q, a)$ is to be q for each state q. If, furthermore, Y has an identity element b, then $\lambda(q, a)$ is to be b for each state q.

In each of the examples to follow, the three sets $\Sigma = \{I^1, \ldots, I^a\}$, $\Delta = \{E^1, \ldots, E^b\}$, and K are nonempty and finite. The elements of Σ, Δ, and K are called *basic inputs*, *basic outputs*, and *states*, respectively.

EXAMPLE 1. Let W and Y be the free semigroups with identity ϵ generated by Σ and Δ, respectively. For each state q and each basic input I, let $\delta(q, I)$ be in K and $\lambda(q, I)$ in Y. Thus $\lambda(q, I)$ is a (possibly empty) *sequence* of basic outputs. Extend δ and λ to satisfy axioms (3) and (4). Then $S = (K, W, Y, \delta, \lambda)$ is an abstract machine.

Machine S is the generalized sequential machine defined in exercise 4 of Section 1.2. It describes the physical situation where a basic input yields a *sequence* of basic outputs, as in a data-processing system. One interpretation of the output ϵ is as the "silent" output. That is, if a basic input I to a machine at state q yields no visible output, write $\lambda(q, I) = \epsilon$. Under this interpretation, the symbol ϵ does not appear in the printed record of the sequence of outputs from the machine.

The remaining examples depend upon semigroups which are defined by "sets of relations."

Notation. Let D be a nonempty set and M the free semigroup generated by D. Let $A = \{(x_\alpha, y_\alpha) | \alpha\}$ be a set of unordered pairs of elements of M, called a *set of relations*. For each pair of elements x and y in M, write xAy if $x = y$ or if there exists some (x_α, y_α) in A such that $x = x_1 x_\alpha x_2$ (x_1 or x_2 may be missing) and $y = x_1 y_\alpha x_2$. For x and y in M write $x \equiv y$ if there exists a finite sequence $x = z_0, \ldots, z_k = y$ of elements in M such that $z_i A z_{i+1}$ for each i.

It is readily verified that $\equiv$ is an equivalence relation.

Theorem 3.1. Let M be the free semigroup generated by a nonempty set D. Let A be a set of relations and N the set of equivalence classes obtained from the equivalence relation generated by A. For two equivalence classes F and G define $F \circ G$ (written FG) to be the equivalence class containing xy, where x is an element of F and y of G. Then N, under the operation of $\circ$ is a semigroup. If an element e is added to N with the property that $e \circ e = e$ and $e \circ F = F \circ e = F$ for each element F in N, then $N \cup \{e\}$, under the operation of $\circ$, is a semigroup with identity e.

---

* Only Theorem 3.1 in this section is used in the sequel.

EXERCISE 1. Prove Theorem 3.1.

Definition 3.3. The semigroup $N(N \cup \{e\})$ of Theorem 3.1 is called the *semigroup (with identity) generated by* D *subject to the set of relations* A.

Each relation (x_α, y_α) in a set of relations is written as $x_\alpha = y_\alpha$. The elements of the semigroup N are customarily denoted by elements of M with the agreement that two elements in the same equivalence class are identified. The importance of Theorem 3.1 is that it provides a universal method for obtaining a semigroup with preassigned dependencies.

We now resume our presentation of examples of quasimachines and abstract machines which model some aspect of a data-processing system.

EXAMPLE 2. Let W be the free semigroup with identity generated by Σ. Let Y be the semigroup with identity generated by Δ subject to the relations $E^i X = X$ for each basic output E^i and for all sequences X of basic outputs of length exactly n, n being a preassigned integer. For each state q and each basic input I let $\delta(q, I)$ be in K and $\lambda(q, I)$ be in Δ. Extend δ and λ to satisfy axioms (3) and (4) of Definition 3.1. Then $S = (K, W, Y, \delta, \lambda)$ is an abstract machine.

For each state q and each sequence $I_1 \ldots I_{k+n}$ of basic inputs,

$$\lambda(q, I_1 \ldots I_{k+n}) = E_{k+1} \ldots E_{k+n},$$

where

$$E_{k+1} \ldots E_{k+n} = \lambda[\delta(q, I_1 \ldots I_k), I_{k+1} \ldots I_{k+n}].$$

This example models the situation where, at each instant, only the last n basic outputs are of interest and are to be retained. Quite often special display devices are used to exhibit the last n basic outputs. Probably the most famous of these devices is the news sign on top of the New York Times Building in New York City.

EXAMPLE 3. Let W be the free semigroup generated by Σ. Let Δ contain at least two elements. Let Y be the semigroup generated by Δ subject to the relations $E^i E^1 = E^1$ for each $i \neq 2$. Let $\delta(q, I)$ be in K and $\lambda(q, I)$ in Δ for each state q and each basic input I. Extend δ and λ in the usual manner. Then $S = (K, W, Y, \delta, \lambda)$ is an abstract machine.

The output E^1 acts as an "erase left to the last E^2" of the recorded outputs. The output E^2 acts as a permanent seal on the outputs produced earlier. An application to data processing of such an E^1 and E^2 is found in the execution of a long scientific problem. Suppose that there are several check points. If agreement occurs at a particular check point, then the output E^2 is listed. If a discrepancy occurs at a check point, then all the outputs recorded since the posting of the last E^2, that is, since the last agreement, are erased and the symbol E^1 inserted. (The symbol E^1 thus indicates that an erasure has transpired.)

Consider the existence of an "erase-right" output, i.e., the existence of E^1 such that $E^1E^i = E^1$ for $i \neq 2$. Such a symbol would find application when one wished to retain only the outputs occurring after the first appearance of E^2. Here E^2 serves as the "start-recording" or "turn-on" output signal. A semigroup containing such a symbol does not satisfy the left cancellation law since $E^1E^1 = E^1E^3 = E^1$ and $E^1 \neq E^3$. This particular situation would thus be an occurrence of a quasimachine which is not an abstract machine.

In each of the examples presented so far the input semigroup was free of relations. In the next two this will no longer be true.

EXAMPLE 4. Let $S = (K, W, Y, \delta, \lambda)$ be any abstract machine, e.g., any of those in the previous examples. For each I and J in W, write $I \sim J$ if $\lambda(q, I) = \lambda(q, J)$ and $\delta(q, I) = \delta(q, J)$ for each state q. The relation $\sim$ is an equivalence relation. For each I in W let I^* be the equivalence class containing I. For two equivalence classes I^* and J^*, define I^*J^* to be $(IJ)^*$. It is readily seen that the equivalence classes form a semigroup W^*. For each state q in K, define $\delta_T(q, I^*)$ to be $\delta(q, I)$ and $\lambda_T(q, I^*)$ to be $\lambda(q, I)$. Clearly $T = (K, W^*, Y, \delta_T, \lambda_T)$ is an abstract machine.

For any two elements I^* and J^* of W^*, there is a state q such that either $\delta_T(q, I^*) \neq \delta_T(q, J^*)$ or $\lambda_T(q, I^*) \neq \lambda_T(q, J^*)$. In the language of data processing, if we regard elements of W as programs of S, and if the two routines I and J always yield the same answer and the same terminal state, then $I \sim J$. Machine S thus becomes machine T if one ignores "equivalent" programs, that is, if one freely interchanges "equivalent" routines. Thus T is the machine which results when the "redundancies" in the inputs, as measured by Y, are factored out of S.

EXAMPLE 5. Let W and Y be the semigroups generated by $II = I$ and $EE = E$ for each basic input I and each basic output E, respectively. If Δ contains at least two elements, then Y does not satisfy the left cancellation law, for $E^1E^2 = E^1E^1E^2$, whereas $E^2 \neq E^1E^2$. Let $S = (K, W, Y, \delta, \lambda)$ be a quasimachine such that $\lambda(q, I)$ is in Δ for each state q and each basic input I. Obviously S is not an abstract machine.

The above quasimachine is pertinent to certain so-called "unclocked" devices in engineering. In these devices, time is not divided into discrete units. A new input is recognized as another input only if it is different from the previous input. (Physically, for example, this means that two consecutive high voltages cannot be distinguished from one high voltage.)

EXERCISE 2. For each state q and each basic input I of the quasi-machine in example 5, show that (i) $\delta(q, I) = \delta[\delta(q, I), I]$, and (ii) $\lambda(q, I) = \lambda[\delta(q, I), I]$.

The final example deals with a situation which is modeled by both an abstract machine and a quasimachine which is not an abstract machine.

EXAMPLE 6. Suppose that $S_1 = (K_1, \Sigma, \Delta, \delta_1, \lambda_1)$ is an incomplete sequential machine. The behavior of S_1 may be modeled by a quasimachine S_2 as follows.

Let $K_2 = K_1 \cup \{q_t\}$, where q_t is a symbol not in K_1. Let W be the free semigroup with identity generated by Σ. Let η be a symbol not in Δ and let Y be the semigroup with identity generated by $\Delta \cup \{\eta\}$ subject to the relations $E\eta = \eta E = \eta$ for all elements E in $\Delta \cup \{\eta\}$. Y does not satisfy the left cancellation law, for if E is in Δ, then $\eta\eta = \eta E = \eta$ but $\eta \neq E$. For q in K_2 and I in Σ, let $\delta_2(q, I) = \delta_1(q, I)$ if $\delta_1(q, I)$ exists, and let $\delta_2(q, I) = q_t$ otherwise. For q in K_2 and I in Σ, let $\lambda_2(q, I) = \lambda_1(q, I)$ if $\lambda_1(q, I)$ exists, and let $\lambda_2(q, I) = \eta$ otherwise. Extend δ_2 and λ_2 to satisfy axioms (3) and (4) of Definition 3.1. Then the quasimachine $S_2 = (K_2, W, Y, \delta_2, \lambda_2)$ has the following two properties for each state q in K_1 and each nonempty sequence $I_1 \ldots I_k$ of basic inputs:

(i) $\delta_2(q, I_1 \ldots I_k) \neq q_t$ if and only if $\delta_1(q, I_1 \ldots I_k)$ exists; and if $\delta_2(q, I_1 \ldots I_k) \neq q_t$, then $\delta_2(q, I_1 \ldots I_k) = \delta_1(q, I_1 \ldots I_k)$.

(ii) $\lambda_2(q, I_1 \ldots I_k) \neq \eta$ if and only if $\lambda_1(q, I_1 \ldots I_k)$ exists; and if $\lambda_2(q, I_1 \ldots I_k) \neq \eta$, then $\lambda_2(q, I_1 \ldots I_k) = \lambda_1(q, I_1 \ldots I_k)$.

Thus S_2 reflects the behavior of S_1 in two senses. If S_1 has a next state, then S_2 yields the same next state; otherwise S_2 goes to the special state q_t. If S_1 yields an output sequence, then S_2 yields the same output sequence; otherwise S_2 yields the special output symbol η.

The behavior of S_1 is modeled, in a sense slightly different from above, by an abstract machine $S_3 = (K_2, W, Y_3, \delta_2, \lambda_3)$ thus. S_3 is defined as is S_2 with the exception that the relations in Y_3 are $E\eta = \eta$ (instead of $E\eta = \eta$ and $\eta E = \eta$) for all elements E in $\Delta \cup \{\eta\}$. Since Y_3 satisfies the left cancellation law, S_3 is an abstract machine. For each state q in K_2 and each nonempty sequence $I_1 \ldots I_k$ of elements of Σ, S_3 satisfies (i) above and the following:

(iii) $\lambda_3(q, I_1 \ldots I_k) = \eta D$ is false for every output sequence D (including the empty one) if and only if $\lambda_1(q, I_1 \ldots I_k)$ exists; and if $\lambda_3(q, I_1 \ldots I_k) = \eta D$ is false for every D, then $\lambda_3(q, I_1 \ldots I_k) = \lambda_1(q, I_1 \ldots I_k)$.

S_3 reflects S_1 as follows. If S_1 has a next state, then S_3 yields the same state; otherwise S_3 goes to the special state q_t. If S_1 yields an output sequence, then S_3 yields the same output sequence; otherwise S_3 yields an output sequence beginning with η.

	I^1	I^2
q_1	$q_1\ I^1$	$q_1\ I^2$
q_2	$q_2\ I^2$	$q_2\ I^1$

	I^1	I^2
p_1	$p_2\ I^1$	$p_2\ I^2$
p_2	$p_1\ I^1$	$p_1\ I^1$

FIGURE 3.1   FIGURE 3.2

Unsolved problem. What structure should be added to an abstract machine to obtain a "topological" machine, as, for example, an analog computer? Presumably K, W, and Y should be topological spaces, with δ and λ, perhaps, being continuous functions.

Unsolved problem (for those familiar with Turing machines). Is there any way to view a Turing machine as an abstract machine?

3.3 Equivalence. The notion of equivalence of states in sequential machines is now generalized to abstract machines.

Definition 3.4. Let

$$S = (K_S, W, Y_S, \delta_S, \lambda_S) \qquad \text{and} \qquad T = (K_T, W, Y_T, \delta_T, \lambda_T)$$

be quasimachines. A state p in S is said to be *equivalent* to a state q in T, written $p \equiv q$, if $\lambda_S(p, I) = \lambda_T(q, I)$ for each I in W. The quasimachines S and T are said to be *equivalent* if to each state p in S there is an equivalent state in T, and to each state q in T an equivalent state in S. A quasimachine is said to be *distinguished* if no two states in it are equivalent.

In dealing with equivalence of states or equivalence of quasimachines, we frequently have to restrict the discussion to abstract machines in order to obtain meaningful results. As an illustration, Lemma 1.1 does not carry over to quasimachines.

EXAMPLE 1. Let $S = (K, W, Y, \delta_S, \lambda_S)$ and $T = (K, W, Y, \delta_T, \lambda_T)$, where $W = Y$ is the semigroup generated by I^1 and I^2 subject to the relations $I^1 I^1 = I^1 I^2$ and $I^2 I^2 = I^2 I^1$; and δ_S, λ_S, δ_T, and λ_T are given in Figs. 3.1 and 3.2, respectively (for a generating set). Then S and T are quasimachines which are not abstract machines. Consider states q_1 and p_1. For any element $I^i J$ in W, $\lambda_S(q_1, I^i J) = \lambda_T(p_1, I^i J) = I^i \ldots I^i$. Thus $q_1 \equiv p_1$. However, $q_1 = \delta_S(q_1, I^1)$ and $p_2 = \delta_T(p_1, I^1)$ are not equivalent states.

The pathology in the previous example arises because Y does not satisfy the left cancellation law. It disappears when the left cancellation property is added to Y.

Lemma 3.1. Let S and T be abstract machines. If state q in S is equivalent to state p in T, then for every element J in W, $\delta_S(q, J)$ is equivalent to $\delta_T(p, J)$.

Proof. Let I be any element of W. Since q and p are equivalent, $\lambda_S(q, J)$ $= \lambda_T(p, J)$ and $\lambda_S(q, JI) = \lambda_T(p, JI)$. Then

$$\lambda_S(q, J)\lambda_S[\delta_S(q, J), I] = \lambda_S(q, JI)$$
$$= \lambda_T(p, JI)$$
$$= \lambda_T(p, J)\lambda_T[\delta_T(p, J), I]$$
$$= \lambda_S(q, J)\lambda_T[\delta_T(p, J), I].$$

Since S and T are machines, Y satisfies the left cancellation law. Thus $\lambda_S[\delta_S(q, J), I] = \lambda_T[\delta_T(p, J), I]$. As I is arbitrary, $\delta_S(q, J)$ is equivalent to $\delta_T(p, J)$.*

The generalization of Theorem 1.3 also holds.

Definition 3.5. Two quasimachines S and T are said to be *isomorphic* if $W_S = W_T$ and there exists a one-to-one mapping f of K_S onto K_T such that for each q in K_S and each element I in W, $\lambda_S(q, I) = \lambda_T[f(q), I]$ and $f[\delta_S(q, I)] = \delta_T[f(q), I]$.

Theorem 3.2. To each abstract machine S there corresponds a unique (up to isomorphism), distinguished machine which is equivalent to S.

Proof. Let $W_T = W_S$ and $Y_T = Y_S$. Let K_T be the set of equivalence classes generated by the equivalence relation $\equiv$ in S. For each element A in K_T and each I in W, define $\lambda_T(A, I)$ to be $\lambda_S(q, I)$ and $\delta_T(A, I)$ to be $[\delta_S(q, I)]$, where q is some element of A. Since the elements in A are equivalent to each other, λ_T is uniquely defined. By Lemma 3.1, δ_T is uniquely defined. Since δ_S and λ_S satisfy axioms (3) and (4) in Definition 3.1, δ_T and λ_T do also. Thus $T = (K_T, W_T, Y_T, \delta_T, \lambda_T)$ is a machine. It is easily seen that T is distinguished and is equivalent to S.

Now suppose that U and T are distinguished machines which are equivalent to S. Then U is equivalent to T. For each state p in U let $f(p)$ be a state in T equivalent to p. Since U and T are both distinguished, f is a one-to-one mapping of K_U onto K_T. Using Lemma 3.1, it is readily seen that U and T are isomorphic.

Theorem 3.2 cannot be extended to hold for quasimachines even if the uniqueness condition is dropped.

---

* Compare with Lemma 1.1.

	I^1	I^2
q_1	$q_2 \quad E^3$	$q_2 \quad E^3$
$\bar{q}_1$	$q_3 \quad E^3$	$q_3 \quad E^3$
q_2	$q_4 \quad E^6$	$q_4 \quad E^6$
q_3	$q_4 \quad E^7$	$q_4 \quad E^7$
q_4	$q_2 \quad E^4$	$q_2 \quad E^4$
q_5	$q_3 \quad E^5$	$q_3 \quad E^5$
q_6	$q_1 \quad E^8$	$q_4 \quad E^1$
q_7	$\bar{q}_1 \quad E^9$	$q_5 \quad E^2$

FIGURE 3.3

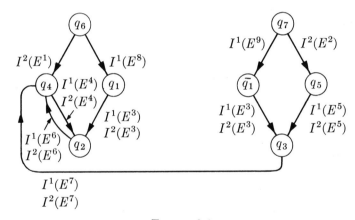

FIGURE 3.4

EXAMPLE 2. Let Y be the semigroup generated by the set of nine
elements $\{E^i | 1 \le i \le 9\}$ subject to the three relations

(1) $E^1E^4 = E^8E^3$, $E^2E^5 = E^9E^3$,   and $E^3E^6 = E^3E^7$.

Let W be the semigroup generated by I^1 and I^2 subject to the relation
$I^1I^1 = I^2I^2$. Let $S = (K, W, Y, \delta, \lambda)$ be the quasimachine, where δ
and λ are given (for a generating set) in Fig. 3.3. The "state-graph"
representation of the table in Fig. 3.3 is found in Fig. 3.4. It is readily
verified that δ and λ are uniquely defined. The only cases to check are
those for which $\delta(q, I^1) \ne \delta(q, I^2)$ and those for which $\lambda(q, I^1) \ne$
$\lambda(q, I^2)$. Then $\delta(q_6, I^1I^1) = \delta(q_6, I^2I^2)$, $\delta(q_7, I^1I^1) = \delta(q_7, I^2I^2)$,

$\lambda(q_6, I^1I^1) = E^8E^3 = E^1E^4 = \lambda(q_6, I^2I^2)$, and $\lambda(q_7, I^1I^1) = E^9E^3 = E^2E^5 = \lambda(q_7, I^2I^2)$.

Suppose that T is a distinguished quasimachine which is equivalent to S. Since S has seven nonequivalent states (only q_1 and $\bar{q}_1$ are equivalent), the states of T may be labeled p_1 to p_7, with p_i equivalent to q_i for each i. Thus $\lambda_T(p_i, I) = \lambda_S(q_i, I)$ for all p_i and all I in W. Consider the next-state function δ_T. First note that

(2)   if $E^xE^y = E^xE$,   where $x, y \leq 9, x \neq 3$,   then $E^y = E$.

Now

$$E^6E^4 = \lambda_T(p_2, I^1I^1)$$
$$= \lambda_T(p_2, I^1)\lambda_T[\delta_T(p_2, I^1), I^1]$$
$$= E^6E,$$

whence $E = E^4$. Since p_4 is the only state p_x such that $\lambda_T(p_x, I^1) = E^6$, $\delta_T(p_2, I^1) = p_4$. Using the same procedure, we see that $\delta_T(p_x, I) = p_y$, where $\delta_S(q_x, I) = q_y$, for (p_x, I) any of the following:

$$(p_2, I^i), (p_3, I^i), (p_4, I^i), (p_5, I^i), (p_6, I^2), (p_7, I^2),   \text{and}   i = 1, 2.$$

Furthermore, $\delta_T(p_6, I^1) = \delta_T(p_7, I^1) = p_1$ since q_1 and $\bar{q}_1$ are each equivalent to p_1. Consider $\delta_T(p_1, I^1)$. It is easily seen that $\delta_T(p_1, I^1)$ is either p_2 or p_3. Suppose that $\delta_T(p_1, I^1) = p_3$. Then

$$\delta_T(p_6, I^1I^1) = \delta_T[\delta_T(p_6, I^1), I^1]$$
$$= \delta_T(p_1, I^1) = p_3.$$

Since $I^1I^1 = I^2I^2$,

$$\delta_T(p_6, I^1I^1) = \delta_T(p_6, I^2I^2)$$
$$= \delta_T[\delta_T(p_6, I^2), I^2]$$
$$= \delta_T(p_4, I^2) = p_2.$$

This is a contradiction. Another contradiction, using p_7, arises if it is assumed that $\delta_T(p_1, I^1) = p_2$. Thus $\delta_T(p_1, I^1)$ cannot be uniquely defined. Therefore T cannot be a quasimachine.

Therefore S is a quasimachine for which there is no equivalent distinguished quasimachine.

EXERCISE 1. Let $S = (K, W, Y, \delta_S, \lambda_S)$, where $W = Y$ is the semigroup generated by I^1 and I^2 subject to the relations $I^1I^1 = I^1I^2$ and $I^2I^2 = I^2I^1$, and δ_S and λ_S are in Fig. 3.5 (for a generating set). (This quasimachine combines the structures of the quasimachines in example 1.)

	I^1	I^2
q_1	$q_1 \quad I^1$	$q_1 \quad I^2$
q_2	$q_2 \quad I^2$	$q_2 \quad I^1$
p_1	$p_2 \quad I^1$	$p_2 \quad I^2$
p_2	$p_1 \quad I^1$	$p_1 \quad I^1$

FIGURE 3.5

Show that there exists a distinguished quasimachine T which is equivalent to S. This example indicates that in constructing a quasimachine S for which there is no equivalent distinguished quasimachine, we cannot select an arbitrary quasimachine having two equivalent states p and q such that $\delta_S(p, I)$ and $\delta_S(q, I)$ are not equivalent.

EXERCISE 2. For each integer $t \leq k$ let $S_t = (K_t, W, Y, \delta_t, \lambda_t)$ be a quasimachine and let K_t be denumerable. Suppose that for every sequence $\{I_i\}$ of elements in W there exists a sequence $\{q_t\}_{t \leq k}$ of states q_t in S_t such that $\lambda_s(q, I_1 \ldots I_i) = \lambda_t(q_t, I_1 \ldots I_i)$ for all s, $t \leq k$, and all i. Prove that there exists a sequence $\{p_t\}_{t \leq k}$ of states p_t in S_t which are equivalent to each other.

EXERCISE 3. Show that exercise 2 is no longer true if there exists an infinite number of quasimachines S_t.

3.4 Input-equivalence. In the previous section we discussed the discrimination between states of a quasimachine by considering the resulting outputs obtained from identical inputs. We now discuss the discrimination between inputs of a quasimachine by considering the resulting outputs obtained from identical states. Again we frequently must restrict the quasimachines to be abstract machines in order to avoid pathological situations.

Definition 3.6. Two inputs I_1 and I_2 of a quasimachine are said to be *input-equivalent** if

$$\lambda(q, I_1) = \lambda(q, I_2) \quad \text{and} \quad \lambda(q, I_1 I) = \lambda(q, I_2 I)$$

for each state q and each input I. A quasimachine is said to be *input-distinguished* if no two distinct inputs are input-equivalent.

* The term "input-indistinguishable" is used in reference [G6].

	I^1	I^2
q_1	q_2 E^1	q_3 E^1
q_2	q_2 E^1	q_2 E^1
q_3	q_3 E^2	q_3 E^2

FIGURE 3.6

The relation of input-equivalence is an equivalence relation.

Suppose that for two inputs I_1 and I_2 and each state q, $\lambda(q, I_1) = \lambda(q, I_2)$ and $\delta(q, I_1) \equiv \delta(q, I_2)$. Then for each input I

$$\lambda(q, I_1 I) = \lambda(q, I_1)\lambda[\delta(q, I_1), I]$$
$$= \lambda(q, I_2)\lambda[\delta(q, I_2), I]$$
$$= \lambda(q, I_2 I).$$

Thus I_1 and I_2 are input-equivalent. The converse is not true. That is, for I_1 and I_2 input-equivalent, it is not necessarily true that $\delta(q, I_1)$ and $\delta(q, I_2)$ are equivalent states.

EXAMPLE 1.   Let W be the free semigroup generated by I^1 and I^2. Let Y be the semigroup generated by E^1 and E^2 subject to the relation $E^1 E^2 = E^1 E^1$. Observe that Y does not satisfy the left cancellation law. Let $K = \{q_1, q_2, q_3\}$. Let δ and λ be given (for a generating set) by Fig. 3.6.   Consider the quasimachine $S = (K, W, Y, \delta, \lambda)$. I^1 and I^2 are input-equivalent, but $\delta(q_1, I^1)$ and $\delta(q_1, I^2)$ are not equivalent states.

The converse is true if S is limited to abstract machines.

Lemma 3.2. Let S be an abstract machine and I_1 and I_2 input-equivalent. Then $\delta(q, I_1)$ and $\delta(q, I_2)$ are equivalent states for each state q. Hence $\delta(q, I_1) = \delta(q, I_2)$ for each state q if S is a distinguished machine.

EXERCISE 1. Prove Lemma 3.2.

Corollary 1. If I_1 and I_2 are input-equivalent in the abstract machine S, and if q_1 and q_2 are equivalent states, then $\delta(q_1, I_1)$ and $\delta(q_2, I_2)$ are equivalent states.

Corollary 2. Let S be an abstract machine. If I_1 and I_2 are input-equivalent and if I_3 and I_4 are input-equivalent, then so are $I_1 I_3$ and $I_2 I_4$.

The proofs of Corollaries 1 and 2 are left to the reader.

The counterpart of Theorem 3.2 for input-equivalence is Theorem 3.3 below. In effect, it asserts that the redundancies in the input semigroup of any abstract machine may be factored out, in essentially one way.

Definition 3.7. Let S and T be quasimachines. T is said to be *input-isomorphic*† to S if there exists an isomorphism h of W_S onto W_T and a one-to-one mapping g of K_S onto K_T with the following properties: For each state q in S and each input I of S, (i) $g[\delta_S(q, I)] = \delta_T[g(q), h(I)]$, and (ii) $\lambda_S(q, I) = \lambda_T[g(q), h(I)]$.

Thus two quasimachines are input-isomorphic if, except for a change in the names of the inputs and the states, they have the same next-state function and the same output function.

Theorem 3.3. To each abstract machine S there corresponds an input-distinguished abstract machine T with the following properties:
(1) $K_S = K_T$.
(2) There exists a homomorphism k of W_S onto W_T such that $\lambda_S(q, I) = \lambda_T[q, k(I)]$ for all inputs I in W_S and each q in K_S.
(3) If S is distinguished, then any input-distinguished abstract machine U satisfying (1) and (2) above is input-isomorphic to T.‡

Proof. For each input I of S let I^* be the equivalence class, generated by the input-equivalence relation, which contains I. For all equivalence classes A and B, define AB to be $(I_1 I_2)^*$ where I_1 and I_2 are arbitrary elements of A and B, respectively. In view of Corollary 2 above, the equivalence class AB is independent of the I_1 and I_2 selected from A and B. The set of equivalence classes under the multiplication just defined obviously is a semigroup. Denote this semigroup by W_T.

Define $\lambda_T(q, A)$ to be $\lambda_S(q, I)$, where I is some element in the equivalence class A. Since the inputs in A are input-equivalent, $\lambda_S(q, I)$ is independent of the I chosen from A. For each state q in S let $[q]$ be the equivalence class, generated by the relation of equivalence between states of S, which contains q. For each equivalence class $[q]$ let p_q be a definite element in $[q]$. Define $\delta_T(q, A)$ to be $p_{v(q)}$, where I is an element of A and $v(q) = \delta_S(q, I)$. By Lemma 3.2, $\delta_T(q, A)$ is independent of the I selected from A.

To prove that $T = (K_S, W_T, Y_S, \delta_T, \lambda_T)$ is a machine, it is sufficient to show that axioms (3) and (4) in Definition 3.1 hold. As to (3), $\delta_T(q, I_1^* I_2^*)$ $= \delta_T(q, (I_1 I_2)^*)$ is an element of $[\delta_S(q, I_1 I_2)]$. Furthermore, $\delta_T(q, I_1^*)$ is in $[\delta_S(q, I_1)]$. Thus $\delta_T(\delta_T(q, I_1^*), I_2^*)$ is in $[\delta_S(\delta_S(q, I_1), I_2)]$. Since $\delta_S(\delta_S(q, I_1), I_2) = \delta_S(q, I_1 I_2)$ and the element p_q of $[q]$ is unique,

---

† The term "widely isomorphic" is used in reference [G6].
‡ Compare with example 4, Section 3.2.

$\delta_T(q, I_1^*I_2^*) = \delta_T(\delta_T(q, I_1^*), I_2^*)$. As to (4),

$$\begin{aligned}
\lambda_T(q, I_1^*I_2^*) &= \lambda_T(q, (I_1I_2)^*) \\
&= \lambda_S(q, I_1I_2) \\
&= \lambda_S(q, I_1)\lambda_S(\delta_S(q, I_1), I_2) \\
&= \lambda_T(q, I_1^*)\lambda_S(\delta_T(q, I_1^*), I_2) \\
&= \lambda_T(q, I_1^*)\lambda_T(\delta_T(q, I_1^*), I_2^*),
\end{aligned}$$

the penultimate equation occurring since $\delta_S(q, I_1) \equiv \delta_T(q, I_1^*)$. Obviously T is input-distinguished.

Let k be the mapping defined by $k(I) = I^*$ for each I in K_S. Clearly k satisfies condition (2) in the conclusion of Theorem 3.3.

Now suppose that S is a distinguished abstract machine. Let U be an input-distinguished abstract machine satisfying (1) and (2) of Theorem 3.3 and let f be the homomorphism of W_S onto W_U. Let g be the identity mapping of $K_T = K_S$ onto $K_U = K_S$, that is, $g(q) = q$ for each q in K_T. Let I_1^* be any element of W_T. Let I_1 and I_2 be any elements of I_1^*. Consider $f(I_1)$ and $f(I_2)$. Since f is a homomorphism of W_S onto W_U, for each element q in K_S,

$$\begin{aligned}
\lambda_U(q, f(I_1)) &= \lambda_S(q, I_1) \\
&= \lambda_S(q, I_2) \\
&= \lambda_U(q, f(I_2));
\end{aligned}$$

and for each I in W_S,

$$\begin{aligned}
\lambda_U(q, f(I_1)f(I)) &= \lambda_U(q, f(I_1I)) \\
&= \lambda_S(q, I_1I) \\
&= \lambda_S(q, I_2I) \\
&= \lambda_U(q, f(I_2I)) \\
&= \lambda_U(q, f(I_2)f(I)).
\end{aligned}$$

Since U is input-distinguished, $f(I_1) = f(I_2)$. Let h be the mapping defined by $h(I_1^*) = f(I_1)$ for any I_1 in I_1^*. Then h is a uniquely defined function of W_T onto W_U. Suppose that $I_1^* \neq I_2^*$. Then I_1 and I_2 are not input-equivalent by definition of I_1^*. If, for some q, $\lambda_S(q, I_1) \neq \lambda_S(q, I_2)$, then $\lambda_U(q, h(I_1^*)) \neq \lambda_U(q, h(I_2^*))$. If $\lambda_S(q, I_1I) \neq \lambda_S(q, I_2I)$ for some q and I, then $\lambda_U(q, h(I_1^*)h(I^*)) \neq \lambda_U(q, h(I_2^*)h(I^*))$. In either case, $h(I_1^*) \neq h(I_2^*)$. Thus h is one-to-one. Since f is a homomorphism of W_S onto W_U,

$$h(I_1^*I_2^*) = h((I_1I_2)^*) = f(I_1I_2) = f(I_1)f(I_2) = h(I_1^*)h(I_2^*).$$

Therefore h is an isomorphism of W_T onto W_U.

To show that T and U are input-isomorphic, it is sufficient to show that $q_1 = \delta_T(q, I_1^*) = \delta_U(q, h(I_1^*)) = q_2$ for each q and each I_1^*. Now $\lambda_T(q, I_1^*) = \lambda_U(q, h(I_1^*))$ and

$$\lambda_T(q, I_1^*)\lambda_T(\delta_T(q, I_1^*), I^*) = \lambda_T(q, I_1^*I^*) = \lambda_U(q, h(I_1^*)h(I^*))$$
$$= \lambda_U(q, h(I_1^*))\lambda_U(\delta_U(q, h(I_1^*)), h(I^*)).$$

As the semigroup $Y_T = Y_S$ satisfies the left cancellation law,

$$\lambda_T(\delta_T(q, I_1^*), I^*) = \lambda_U(\delta_U(q, h(I_1^*)), h(I^*))$$

for each I^* in W_T. Then

$$\lambda_S(q_1, I) = \lambda_T(q_1, I^*) = \lambda_U(q_2, h(I^*)) = \lambda_T(q_2, I^*) = \lambda_S(q_2, I).$$

Thus $q_1 \equiv q_2$. Since S is distinguished, $q_1 = q_2$.

Observe in the preceding theorem that even if S is a complete sequential machine, T might not be one (see exercise 4). Thus when considering the removal of equivalent sequences of inputs from complete sequential machines, we recognize a need for a more general kind of device, such as an abstract machine.

By an obvious modification of Theorem 3.3, the following result about sequential machines is seen to hold.

Theorem 3.4. To each complete sequential machine S there corresponds a complete sequential machine T with the following properties:

(1) $K_S = K_T$.

(2)   There exists a homomorphism k of W_S onto W_T such that $\lambda_S(q, I) = \lambda_T(q, k(I))$ for all inputs I in W_S and each state q.

(3)   No two elements of Σ_T are input-equivalent.

(4)   If S is distinguished, then any complete sequential machine satisfying (1), (2), and (3) is input-isomorphic to T.

Exercise 2. Prove Theorem 3.4.

Exercise 3. Show that the machine T specified by Theorem 3.4 need not be input-distinguished.

Unsolved problem. Let S be a complete sequential machine with n states. It is known [G6] that there exists an integer k such that for each state q in S, if no two distinct tapes $I_1 \ldots I_k$ and $J_1 \ldots J_k$ are input-equivalent, then S is input-distinguished. Find the smallest such integer k in terms of n, $\#(\Sigma)$, and $\#(\Delta)$.

The unsolved problem is concerned with determining a sufficient condition for a sequential machine to be input-distinguished. A necessary condition for S to be input-distinguished is given below. It places an upper bound on the number of elements of Σ in terms of the number of states and number of outputs.

Lemma 3.3. Let S be a complete sequential machine with $n = \#(K)$ and $m = \#(\Delta)$. Suppose that C is a subset of Σ containing r elements, where $(m^k n)^n < r^k$ for some positive integer k. Then there exist two sequences $A_1 \ldots A_k$ and $B_1 \ldots B_k$ of elements in C which are input-equivalent.

Proof. Denote the elements of K by $p_1, \ldots, p_n$. To each nonempty sequence $I = I_1 \ldots I_k$ of elements in C, associate the n-tuple of triples

$$\tau_I = ((p_1, q_1, E_1), (p_2, q_2, E_2), \ldots, (p_n, q_n, E_n)),$$

where $q_i = \delta(p_i, I)$ and $E_i = \lambda(p_i, I)$ for each i. Since $m = \#(\Delta)$ and $n = \#(K)$, there are at most $(m^k n)^n$ different τ_I. As there are $r^k > (m^k n)^n$ different I, two of the associated n-tuples, say τ_I and τ_J, are identical. Then I and J are input-equivalent since $\delta(p_i, I) = \delta(p_i, J)$ and $\lambda(p_i, I) = \lambda(p_i, J)$ for each state p.

Theorem 3.5. Let S be a complete sequential machine, with $n = \#(K_S)$, $r = \#(\Sigma_S)$, and $m = \#(\Delta_S)$. If $m^n < r$, then S is not input-distinguished. If $r \leq m^n$, then there exists a complete input-distinguished sequential machine T with $n = \#(K_T)$, $r = \#(\Sigma_T)$, and $m = \#(\Delta_T)$.

Proof. Let S be a complete sequential machine for which $m^n < r$. Since $1 < r/m^n$, there exists a positive integer k such that $n^n < r^k/m^{nk}$. Then $(m^k n)^n < r^k$. By Lemma 3.3, there exist sequences $A_1 \ldots A_k$ and $B_1 \ldots B_k$ of elements of Σ_S which are input-equivalent. Consequently S is not input-distinguished.

Now suppose that $r \leq m^n$. Let $p_1, \ldots, p_n$ be n distinct symbols and let $K_T = \{p_i | i \leq n\}$. Let $E^1, \ldots, E^m$ be m distinct symbols and let $\Delta_T = \{E^i | i \leq m\}$. Let D_T be a set of r distinct n-tuples τ having the form

$$\tau = ((p_1, p_1, E_1), (p_2, p_2, E_2), \ldots, (p_n, p_n, E_n)),$$

where each E_i is in Δ_T. The set D_T exists, since $r \leq m^n$. To each τ in D_T, associate a distinct symbol I_τ, and let $\Sigma_T = \{I_\tau | \tau \text{ in } D_T\}$. For each $i \leq n$, define $\delta_T(p_i, I_\tau) = p_i$ and $\lambda_T(p_i, I_\tau) = E_i$, where (p_i, p_i, E_i) is the ith coordinate in τ. Then $T = (K_T, \Sigma_T, \Delta_T, \delta_T, \lambda_T)$ is a complete sequential machine, with $n = \#(K_T)$, $m = \#(\Delta_T)$, and $r = \#(\Sigma_T)$.

Let $A_1 \ldots A_s$ and $B_1 \ldots B_s$ be two nonempty sequences of elements of Σ_T. Suppose that A_t is the first A_i such that $A_t \neq B_t$, but $A_i = B_i$ for $i < t$. Then $A_t = I_\sigma$ and $B_t = I_\tau$, with $\sigma \neq \tau$. For some integer, say j, the jth coordinate (p_j, p_j, E_j) of σ differs from the jth coordinate (p_j, p_j, E_j^*) of τ. Then $E_j \neq E_j^*$. From this it follows that $\lambda_T(p_j, A_1 \ldots A_s) \neq \lambda_T(p_j, B_1 \ldots B_s)$. Therefore T is input-distinguished.

The previous result gives a necessary condition in terms of $\#(K)$, $\#(\Sigma)$, and $\#(\Delta)$ in order for a complete sequential machine to be input-distinguished, that is, no two inputs be input-equivalent. Suppose a necessary condition is wanted so that no two basic inputs, i.e., elements of Σ, are input-equivalent.

Theorem 3.6. Let S be a complete sequential machine, with $n = \#(K_S)$ and $m = \#(\Delta_S)$. Then every set of $(mn)^n + 1$ elements of Σ_S contains two which are input-equivalent. Furthermore, if $m \geq 2$, then there exists a distinguished complete sequential machine T such that $n = \#(K_T)$, $m = \#(\Delta_T)$, $(mn)^n = \#(\Sigma_T)$, and no two elements of Σ_T are input-equivalent.

Proof. The first part of the theorem follows from Lemma 3.3 with $k = 1$. As to the second part, let $m \geq 2$ and n be given positive integers. Let $p_1, \ldots, p_n$ be n distinct symbols and $K_T = \{p_i | i \leq n\}$. Let $E^1, \ldots, E^m$ be m distinct elements and $\Delta_T = \{E^i | i \leq m\}$. Let D_T be the set of all $(mn)^n$ distinct n-tuples τ having the form

$$\tau = \big((p_1, q_1, E_1), (p_2, q_2, E_2), \ldots, (p_n, q_n, E_n)\big),$$

where q_i is in K_T and E_i is in Δ_T for each i. To each τ in D_T, associate a symbol I_τ and let $\Sigma_T = \{I_\tau | \tau \text{ in } D_T\}$. Define $\delta_T(p_i, I_\tau) = q_i$ and $\lambda_T(p_i, I_\tau) = E_i$, where (p_i, q_i, E_i) is the ith coordinate in τ. Then $T = (K_T, \Sigma_T, \Delta_T, \delta_T, \lambda_T)$ is a complete sequential machine such that $\#(\Sigma_T) = (mn)^n$, $\#(K_T) = n$, and $\#(\Delta_T) = m$.

Let E^1 and E^2 be distinct elements of Δ_T. E^1 and E^2 exist since $\#(\Delta_T) \geq 2$. Suppose that p_i and p_j are distinct states of T, with $i < j$. Let v be the n-tuple.

$$v = \big((p_1, p_1, E^1), \ldots, (p_i, p_i, E^1), (p_{i+1}, p_{i+1}, E^2), \ldots, (p_n, p_n, E^2)\big).$$

Then $\lambda_T(p_i, I_v) = E^1 \neq E^2 = \lambda_T(p_j, I_v)$. Therefore p_i and p_j are not equivalent states, i.e., T is a distinguished machine.

Finally, let I_σ and I_τ be distinct elements of Σ_T. Let i be the smallest integer such that the ith coordinate (p_i, q_i, E_i) in σ is not identical with the ith coordinate $(p_i, \bar{q}_i, \bar{E}_i)$ in τ. Two cases arise.

(i) $E_i \neq \bar{E}_i$. Then $\lambda(p_i, I_\sigma) \neq \lambda(p_i, I_\tau)$.

(ii) $E_i = \bar{E}_i$. Then $q_i \neq \bar{q}_i$. As shown above, there exists an element I_v of Σ_T such that $\lambda(q_i, I_v) \neq \lambda(\bar{q}_i, I_v)$. Thus $\lambda(p_i, I_\sigma I_v) \neq \lambda(p_i, I_\tau I_v)$.

In either case it follows that I_σ and I_τ are not input-equivalent. Thus no two elements of Σ_T are input-equivalent.

	I^1	I^2	I^3
p_1	p_1 E^1	p_2 E^1	p_2 E^3
p_2	p_2 E^2	p_1 E^2	p_2 E^3

FIGURE 3.7

EXERCISE 4. Let S be the complete sequential machine in Fig. 3.7. Show

$$\text{(i)} \quad I^1 \not\equiv I^2;$$

$$\text{(ii)} \quad I^1 I^3 \equiv I^2 I^3.$$

Prove each of the following.

EXERCISE 5. The following analog to Theorem 3.6 is *not* true: If S is a distinguished complete sequential machine, with $\#(\Sigma) = n$ and $\#(\Delta) = m$, then $\#(K) \leq f(m, n)$, $f(m, n)$ being a finite number depending only on m and n.

EXERCISE 6. A quasimachine T is said to be a *semi-inverse* of the quasimachine S if the following conditions are satisfied:
  (i) $Y_S = W_T$.
  (ii) $Y_T = W_S$.
  (iii) For each state q in S there is a state $g(q)$ in T such that

$$\lambda_T[g(q), \lambda_S(q, I)] = I$$

for all I in W_S.
  (iv) For each state p in T there is a state $h(p)$ in S such that

$$\lambda_S[h(p), \lambda_T(p, J)] = J$$

for all J in W_T.
  If U and V are semi-inverses of S and T, respectively, and if p in S and q in T are equivalent states, then $g_S(p)$ and $g_T(q)$ are equivalent states.

EXERCISE 7. Let T be a semi-inverse of the quasimachine S. A quasimachine U is a semi-inverse of S if and only if U and T are equivalent.

EXERCISE 8. T is said to be an *inverse* of S if (i) T is a semi-inverse of S, and (ii) $g[\delta_S(q, I)] = \delta_T[g(q), \lambda_S(q, I)]$ for each q in K_S and I in W_S. If T is a distinguished machine which is a semi-inverse of S, then T is an inverse of S.

EXERCISE 9. If T and U are both distinguished quasimachines which are inverses of S, then T and U are isomorphic to each other.

EXERCISE 10. A necessary and sufficient condition that a quasimachine have an inverse is that for each state q, λ_S be a one-to-one function of W_S onto Y_S.

3.5 Synthesis. The term "synthesis" refers to the construction of a system which satisfies certain specifications. We now consider the problem of finding an abstract machine $(K, W, Y, \delta, \lambda)$ when the semigroup W is specified. One such trivial machine always exists. This is the machine in which K consists of the single state q_1, Y consists of one element E, and $\delta(q_1, I) = q_1$ and $\lambda(q_1, I) = E$ for each I in W. This machine is degenerate in the sense that each two inputs are input-equivalent. Therefore let us impose the additional condition that no two inputs are input-equivalent. Thus the problem to be considered is this. Does an arbitrary semigroup serve as the input semigroup of some input-distinguished machine? The answer is "yes" as is now shown.

Theorem 3.7. For each semigroup W there exists an input-distinguished abstract machine $S = (K, W, Y, \delta, \lambda)$.

Proof. For each element I in W let q_I be an abstract symbol. Let q_* be a symbol distinct from each symbol q_I and let

$$K = \{q_*\} \cup \{q_I | I \text{ in } W\}.$$

For each element I in W let I^* be an abstract symbol. Let Y be the semigroup generated by the set $\{I^* | I \text{ in } W\}$ subject to the relations $I^*J^* = J^*$ for all I^* and J^*. Then Y satisfies the left cancellation law. Let δ and λ be the functions defined by $\delta(q_*, I) = q_I$, $\delta(q_J, I) = q_{JI}$, $\lambda(q_*, I) = I^*$, and $\lambda(q_J, I) = (JI)^*$ for all I and J in W.

Consider the function δ.

$$\delta(q_*, IJ) = q_{IJ}$$

and

$$\delta[\delta(q_*, I), J] = \delta(q_I, J) = q_{IJ},$$

while

$$\delta(q_M, IJ) = q_{MIJ}$$

and

$$\delta[\delta(q_M, I), J] = \delta(q_{MI}, J) = q_{MIJ}.$$

Consider the function λ.

$$\lambda(q_*, IJ) = (IJ)^*$$

and

$$\lambda(q_*, I)\lambda[\delta(q_*, I), J] = I^*(IJ)^* = (IJ)^*,$$

while

$$\lambda(q_M, IJ) = (MIJ)^*$$

and

$$\lambda(q_M, I)\lambda[\delta(q_M, I), J] = (MI)^*(MIJ)^* = (MIJ)^*.$$

Thus δ and λ satisfy axioms (3) and (4) in Definition 3.1. Therefore $S = (K, W, Y, \delta, \lambda)$ is an abstract machine. For $I \neq J$, $\lambda(q_*, I) \neq \lambda(q_*, J)$. Hence no two elements in W are input-equivalent. Thus S is input-distinguished.

EXERCISE 1. Let W be the semigroup generated by I^1, I^2, I^3, I^4 with the relations $I^iI^j = I^i$ and $I^iI^4 = I^4$ for $i = 1, 2, 3, 4$ and $j = 1, 2, 3$. Using Theorem 3.7, find an input-distinguished abstract machine

$$(K, W, Y, \delta, \lambda).$$

The proof of Theorem 3.7 always produces an input-distinguished abstract machine $(K, W, Y, \delta, \lambda)$ for a given semigroup W. In addition, the machine produced always has an *infinite* number of states whenever W is infinite. The question naturally arises as to whether or not a finite-state machine can always be found when W is infinite. The example below answers this negatively even when W is generated by a finite number of elements and a finite number of relations.

EXAMPLE 1. Let W be the semigroup generated by the finite set $\{I_1, I_2, I_3\}$ and the two relations $I_1I_2 = I_1I_3$ and $I_1I_1I_2 = I_1I_2I_1$. An immediate consequence of the two relations is that $I_1I_1I_3 = I_1I_3I_1$. We shall show that there is no finite-state, input-distinguished, abstract machine $(K, W, Y, \delta, \lambda)$.

(a) $(I_1)^n(I_2)^n = (I_1)^n(I_3)^n = (I_1I_2)^n$ for all n. To see this, observe that $I_1I_1I_2I_2 = I_1I_2I_1I_2$. Using mathematical induction, suppose that for $k \leq m$, (i) $(I_1)^k(I_2)^k = (I_1I_2)^k$ and (ii) $I_1(I_1I_2)^k = (I_1I_2)^kI_1$. Then

$$(I_1)^{m+1}(I_2)^{m+1} = I_1[(I_1)^m(I_2)^m]I_2 = I_1(I_1I_2)^mI_2$$
$$= (I_1I_2)^mI_1I_2 = (I_1I_2)^{m+1};$$

and

$$I_1(I_1I_2)^{m+1} = I_1I_1I_2(I_1I_2)^m = I_1I_2I_1(I_1I_2)^m$$
$$= (I_1I_2)(I_1I_2)^mI_1 = (I_1I_2)^{m+1}I_1.$$

Thus (i) and (ii) hold for all integers m. Similarly $(I_1)^m(I_3)^m = (I_1I_3)^m$ and $I_1(I_1I_3)^m = (I_1I_3)^mI_1$ for all integers m. Then $(I_1)^n(I_2)^n = (I_1I_2)^n = (I_1I_3)^n = (I_1)^n(I_3)^n$ for all integers n.

(b) $(I_1)^n(I_2)^{n+1} = (I_1)^n(I_3)^{n+1}$ for no integer n. The reasoning is as follows. By (a), $(I_1)^n(I_2)^{n+1} = (I_1I_2)^nI_2$ and $(I_1)^n(I_3)^{n+1} = (I_1I_3)^nI_3 = (I_1I_2)^nI_3$. Assume that (b) is false. Then there is an integer n so that $(I_1I_2)^nI_2 = (I_1I_2)^nI_3$. Let $N_1, N_2, \ldots, N_p$ be any proof of this last relation. That is, let $N_1, \ldots, N_p$ be a finite sequence of words such that N_1 is $(I_1I_2)^nI_2$, N_p is $(I_1I_2)^nI_3$, and N_{i+1} is obtained from N_i by substitution of (i) I_1I_3 for I_1I_2, or (ii) I_1I_2 for I_1I_3, or (iii) $I_1I_1I_2$ for $I_1I_2I_1$, or (iv) $I_1I_2I_1$ for $I_1I_1I_2$. Let N_r be the first word of the proof such that the right-most symbol occurrence is replaced in passing to the succeeding word of the proof. Clearly each N_i, $1 \le i \le r$, can be written in the form M_iI_2. N_r certainly exists, since N_p is not of this form. Moreover, $M_1, M_2, \ldots, M_r$ is a valid proof of $M_1 = M_r$. Since N_{r+1} must be obtained from N_r by either (i) or (iv), M_r is JI_1 for some J. M_1 is $(I_1I_2)^n$. It will now be shown that the existence of the proof $M_1, M_2, \ldots, M_r$ for $(I_1I_2)^n = JI_1$ leads to a contradiction. Consider the following three properties about the words $M = M_j$:

(1) The number of occurrences of I_1 in M is n.

(2) If M is the word $H_1I_2H_2$ or $H_1I_3H_2$, then H_1 is nonempty and $n_2(H_1) - n_1(H_1) < n_1(H_1)$, where $n_2(X)$ is the length of X and $n_1(X)$ is the number of occurrences of I_1 in X.

(3) M is of length $2n$.

(1) and (3) are obvious. As to (2), it is certainly true for M_1. Suppose that it is true for M_i, $i \le h$. If (i), (ii), or (iii) are used in passing from M_h to M_{h+1}, (2) is still true. Suppose that (iv) is used. That is, let $M_h = PI_1I_1I_2H_2$ and $M_{h+1} = PI_1I_2I_1H_2$. Then

$$n_2(PI_1) - n_1(PI_1) = n_2(PI_1I_1) - n_1(PI_1I_1)$$

and

$$n_1(PI_1) = n_1(PI_1I_1) - 1.$$

By assumption,

$$n_2(PI_1I_1) - n_1(PI_1I_1) < n_1(PI_1I_1) = n_1(PI_1) + 1.$$

Thus

$$n_2(PI_1) - n_1(PI_1) \le n_1(PI_1).$$

Two cases arise.

(α) $n_2(PI_1) - n_1(PI_1) < n_1(PI_1)$. Then (2) is extended to M_{h+1}.

(β) $n_2(PI_1) - n_1(PI_1) = n_1(PI_1)$. Then $n_2(PI_1I_1) - n_1(PI_1I_1) = n_1(PI_1I_1) - 1$. If P consists entirely of occurrences of I_1, then $n_2(PI_1I_1) - n_1(PI_1I_1) + 1 = 1$ and $n_1(PI_1I_1) \ge 2$, a contradiction. Thus P

does not consist entirely of occurrences of I_1. Let X be the right-most symbol which is not I_1, that is, let $P = Q_1XQ_2$, where $Q_2 = (I_1)^d (d \geq 0)$.*
Then $M_h = Q_1XQ_2I_1I_1I_2H_2$, so that $n_2(Q_1) - n_1(Q_1) < n_1(Q_1)$.
Now $n_2(Q_1) = n_2(PI_1I_1) - (3+d)$ and $n_1(Q_1) = n_1(PI_1I_1) - (2+d)$.
Thus

$$n_2(Q_1) - n_1(Q_1) = n_2(PI_1I_1) - n_1(PI_1I_1) - 1$$
$$= n_1(PI_1I_1) - 1 - 1$$
$$\geq n_1(Q_1).$$

This contradicts (2) for M_h. Thus (β) does not occur so that only (α) arises. Hence (2) is true.

We now are in a position to demonstrate part (b) of the example. From (1) and (3), JI_1 is not of the form $(I_1)^k$. Thus JI_1 is either of the form $H_1I_2(I_1)^s$ or $H_1I_3(I_1)^s$. From (1) and (3), $n_1(H_1) = n - s$ and $n_2(H_1) = 2n - s - 1$. Then $n_1(H_1) \leq n - 1 = n_2(H_1) - n_1(H_1)$.
This contradicts (2). Thus the proof $M_1, \ldots, M_r$ of $(I_1I_2)^n = JI_1$ does not exist, demonstrating (b).

(c) There is no finite-state, input-distinguished machine

$$S = (K, W, Y, \delta, \lambda).$$

Consider the contrary. Let $S = (K, W, Y, \delta, \lambda)$ be a finite-state, input-distinguished machine. Consider the sequence of pairs of elements of W whose typical term is $((I_1)^k(I_2)^{k+1}, (I_1)^k(I_3)^{k+1})$. By (b), the two elements in each pair are different elements of W. Now S is input-distinguished and K is finite. Thus there is a state q_0 which distinguishes infinitely many of these pairs.† Hence there is an infinite set A of integers so that for each integer j in A there is an element M_j (possibly empty) of W with the property that

$$\lambda(q_0, (I_1)^j(I_2)^{j+1}M_j) \neq \lambda(q_0, (I_1)^j(I_3)^{j+1}M_j).$$

Let j and k, $j < k$, be two integers in A having the property that $\delta[q_0, (I_1)^j] = \delta[q_0, (I_1)^k]$. Since K is finite, the integers j and k certainly exist. Let $q_1 = \delta[q_0, (I_1)^j]$. Then

$$\delta[q_1, (I_1)^{k-j}] = \delta[\delta(q_0, (I_1)^j), (I_1)^{k-j}] = \delta[q_0, (I_1)^k] = q_1.$$

Hence for any integer m there exists a state q_2 such that $\delta[q_2, (I_1)^m] = q_1$ (merely let $q_2 = \delta[q_1, (I_1)^n]$, where n is chosen so that $n + m$ is a mul-

---

* $(I_1)^0$ is the empty sequence ϵ.

† By q_0 *distinguishing the pair* (I, J) is meant that either $\lambda(q_0, I) \neq \lambda(q_0, J)$ or $\lambda(q_0, I) = \lambda(q_0, J)$, but for some M, $\lambda(q_0, IM) \neq \lambda(q_0, JM)$.

tiple of $k - j$). Thus there exists a state q_3 such that $\delta(q_3, (I_1)^{j+1}) = q_1$. Then

$$\lambda[q_3, (I_1)^{j+1}(I_2)^{j+1}M_j] = \lambda[q_3, (I_1)^{j+1}]\lambda[\delta(q_3, (I_1)^{j+1}), (I_2)^{j+1}M_j]$$
$$= \lambda[q_3, (I_1)^{j+1}]\lambda[q_1, (I_2)^{j+1}M_j].$$

Similarly

$$\lambda[q_3, (I_1)^{j+1}(I_3)^{j+1}M_j] = \lambda[q_3, (I_1)^{j+1}]\lambda[q_1, (I_3)^{j+1}M_j].$$

Since $(I_1)^{j+1}(I_2)^{j+1} = (I_1)^{j+1}(I_3)^{j+1}$,

$$\lambda[q_3, (I_1)^{j+1}]\lambda[q_1, (I_2)^{j+1}M_j] = \lambda[q_3, (I_1)^{j+1}]\lambda[q_1, (I_3)^{j+1}M_j].$$

As left cancellation holds in Y, it follows that

$$\lambda[q_1, (I_2)^{j+1}M_j] = \lambda[q_1, (I_3)^{j+1}M_j].$$

Then

$$\lambda[q_0, (I_1)^{j}(I_2)^{j+1}M_j] = \lambda[q_0, (I_1)^{j}]\lambda[q_1, (I_2)^{j+1}M_j]$$
$$= \lambda[q_0, (I_1)^{j}]\lambda[q_1, (I_3)^{j+1}M_j]$$
$$= \lambda[q_0, (I_1)^{j}(I_3)^{j+1}M_j],$$

contradicting the fact that $\lambda[q_0, (I_1)^{j}(I_2)^{j+1}M_j] \neq \lambda[q_0, (I_1)^{j}(I_3)^{j+1}M_j]$. Therefore S cannot be a finite-state, input-distinguished machine.

EXERCISE 2. Let W be the semigroup generated by the set $\{I^n|n \geq 1\}$ and the relations $I^m I^n = I^k$, where $k = \max\{m, n\}$. Let

$$S = (K, W, Y, \delta, \lambda)$$

be any abstract machine with a finite number of states. Show each of the following.

(a) For each state q there is an infinite subset G_q of W and a state $\bar{q}$ such that $\delta(q, I) = \bar{q}$ for all I in G_q.

Define $H_q = \{I|I$ in W, $\delta(q, I) = \bar{q}\}$.

(b) $\lambda(\bar{q}, I)$ is independent of I in W; that is, $\lambda(\bar{q}, I) = \lambda(\bar{q}, J)$ for all I and J in W.

(c) For $(I)^m$ in H_q and $n > m$, $(I)^n$ is in H_q.

(d) For each state q there is an integer N_q so that $\lambda[q, (I)^n]$ is independent of n for all $n \geq N_q$.

(e) The abstract machine S is not input-distinguished.

Unsolved problem. Find conditions on a semigroup W which guarantee the existence of a finite-state input-distinguished abstract machine

$$S = (K, W, Y, \delta, \lambda).$$

3.6 History. Quasimachines and abstract machines first appear in [G6]. The examples of Section 3.2 are found in [G7]. The material in Section 3.5 is drawn from [G8].

CHAPTER 4

RECOGNITION DEVICES

An important problem in data-processing systems is to define and study so-called (character) recognition devices. That is, suppose there is a given family $\{A_i | 1 \leq i \leq n\}$ of pairwise disjoint sets of so-called "characters." For example, each A_i might be the set of possible versions of the ith letter in the alphabet. It is desired to define a device which will discern to which A_i any character inserted into the device belongs. Thus one might want a device which scans a printed page and recognizes each letter in the text (presumably so as to "code" it and then operate on it). The recognition that a character belongs to a particular A_i may be regarded as the output of the device to the character.

Suppose that each character can be transformed one-to-one into a possibly empty sequence of letters from a finite alphabet. Then the family $\{A_i | 1 \leq i \leq n\}$ may be considered as a family of disjoint sets of tapes. The problem is to obtain a device which determines to which A_i a particular tape belongs. Several such devices are described. The determination is achieved by several means, the main one being by the final state of the device. The sets of tapes for which such a discrimination is possible are also studied.

4.1 Automata. As usual, K is a finite nonempty set whose elements are called *states*. Σ is a finite nonempty set whose elements are called *inputs*. A finite sequence $I_1 \ldots I_k$ of elements of Σ is called a *tape*.* $\theta(\Sigma)$, or θ when Σ is understood, is the set of all tapes formed from elements of Σ. Thus $\theta(\Sigma)$ is the free semigroup with identity ϵ generated by Σ.

A recognition device which discriminates between tapes by the terminal state of the device is now introduced. This "machine" is the most fundamental of the recognition devices presented.

Definition 4.1. An *automaton* is a 5-tuple $A = (K, \Sigma, \delta, s_0, F)$, where
   (i) δ is a function from $K \times \Sigma$ into K (the "next-state" function),
   (ii) s_0 is an element of K (the "start" state),
   (iii) F is a subset of K.

Extend δ to all pairs (q, J) of states q and tapes J as is done in Chapter 1.

Definition 4.2. A tape J is said to be *accepted* by the automaton $A = (K, \Sigma, \delta, s_0, F)$ if $\delta(s_0, J)$ is in F. Denote by $T(A)$ the set of those tapes accepted by A.

---

* As usual, $I_1 \ldots I_k = \epsilon$ if $k = 0$.

An automaton, unlike a sequential machine, does not have an output function.* However, an automaton has other features. These other features consist of a designated start state s_0 and a designated set F of terminal states.

Definition 4.3. A set U of tapes is said to be Σ-*regular*, or *regular* when Σ is understood, if $U = T(A)$ for some automaton $A = (K, \Sigma, \delta, s_0, F)$.

EXAMPLE 1. Let δ be the function in Fig. 4.1.

(a) If $A = (K, \Sigma, \delta, p_1, \{p_2\})$, then $T(A) = \{(I^1)^n | n \geq 1\}$.

(b) If $A = (K, \Sigma, \delta, p_1, \{p_3\})$, then

$$T(A) = \{(I^1)^n I^2 J | n \geq 0, J \text{ any tape}\}.$$

An automaton $A = (K, \Sigma, \delta, s_0, F)$ functions as a recognition device in the following way. Let $U = T(A)$ and $V = \theta - T(A)$. For every tape J, J is in U or J is in V according as $\delta(s_0, J)$ is in F or $K - F$. Thus the automaton discerns between the tapes in U and those in V by its terminal state.

This suggests the following more general recognition device. Let $A = (K, \Sigma, \delta, s_0, G_1, \ldots, G_r)$, where δ and s_0 are as in Definition 4.1, and $G_1, \ldots, G_r$ are disjoint subsets of K. For each i let $U_i = \{X | \delta(s_0, X)$ is in $G_i\}$. Then A is a recognition device of the tapes in $\cup_i U_i$ in the sense that each tape in $\cup_i U_i$ is associated with the appropriate U_i by the terminal state of the device. However, as far as the structure of the sets U_i is concerned, the discussion can be restricted to automata. This is because

(a) each U_i is a regular set (exercise 5 below).

The importance of regular sets to recognition devices is considerable since the converse to (a) is also true. Specifically, let $\{U_i | 1 \leq i \leq r\}$ be a family of pairwise disjoint regular sets. Then

(b) there exists a recognition device $A = (K, \Sigma, \delta, s_0, G_1, \ldots, G_r)$ such that a tape X is in U_i if and only if $\delta(s_0, X)$ is in G_i (exercise 6 below).

From (a) and (b) it is seen that the discriminatory power of a general recognition device $A = (K, \Sigma, \delta, s_0, G_1, \ldots, G_r)$ is intimately related to regular sets. Because of this, our study of recognition devices will consist of investigating the structure of regular sets as well as various extensions of automata.

EXERCISE 1. Let δ be the function in Fig. 4.2. Find $T(A)$, where $A = (K, \Sigma, \delta, p_1, \{p_2\})$.

---

* With each automaton there is associated a "natural" output function λ, namely, $\lambda(q, I) = 1$ if $\delta(q, I)$ is in F and $\lambda(q, I) = 0$ otherwise for each I in Σ.

	I^1	I^2
p_1	p_2	p_3
p_2	p_2	p_3
p_3	p_3	p_3

FIGURE 4.1

	I^1	I^2
p_1	p_2	p_3
p_2	p_2	p_1
p_3	p_3	p_3

FIGURE 4.2

EXERCISE 2. Let $A = (K, \Sigma, \delta_A, q_1, F)$ be a given automaton. Let $B = (K, \Sigma, \delta_A, q_1, G)$, where

$$G = \{\delta_A(q_1, J) \mid \delta_A(q_1, JJ_1) \text{ is in } F \text{ for some tape } J_1\}.$$

Then

$$T(B) = \{J \mid JJ_1 \text{ is in } T(A) \text{ for some tape } J_1\}.$$

EXERCISE 3. Let $A = (K, \Sigma, \delta_A, q_1, F)$ be a given automaton. Let G be as in exercise 2, and let $\{p_i \mid 1 \le i \le r\} = G$. For each i, $1 \le i \le r$, let $B_i = (K, \Sigma, \delta_A, p_i, G)$. Then $\bigcup_1^r T(B_i)$ is the set of those tapes J for which there exist tapes J_1 and J_2 such that J_1JJ_2 is in $T(A)$.

EXERCISE 4. Let $A = (K, \Sigma, \delta_A, q_1, F)$ be a given automaton and q_0 a symbol not in K. Let $B = (K \cup \{q_0\}, \Sigma, \delta_B, q_1, F)$, where $\delta_B(q_0, I) = q_0$, and for q in K, I in Σ, $\delta_B(q, I) = \delta_A(q, I)$ if $\delta_A(q, I)$ is in F, $\delta_B(q, I) = q_0$ otherwise. Then

$$T(B) = \{J \mid J = I_1 \ldots I_k, k \ge 1,$$
$$\text{and for each } 1 \le i \le k, I_1 \ldots I_i \text{ is in } T(A)\}.$$

EXERCISE 5. Prove (a).

EXERCISE 6. Prove (b). [*Hint:* For each i let $A_i = (K_i, \Sigma, \delta_i, s_0^i, F_i)$ be an automaton such that $T(A_i) = U_i$. Let $K = K_1 \times \cdots \times K_r$ and $s_0 = (s_0^1, \ldots, s_0^r)$. Let δ be the mapping of $K \times \Sigma$ into K defined by $\delta((x_1, \ldots, x_r), I) = (\delta_1(x_1, I), \ldots, \delta_r(x_r, I))$ for each $(x_1, \ldots, x_r)$ in K and I in Σ. For each i let $G_i = H_1^i \times \cdots \times H_r^i$, where $H_j^i = K_j - F_j$ or $H_j^i = F_j$ according as $j \ne i$ or $j = i$. Then $\{G_i \mid i \le r\}$ is a family of disjoint subsets of K and a tape J is in U_i if and only if $\delta(s_0, J)$ is in G_i.]

EXERCISE 7. Let $\{U_i \mid 1 \le i \le s\}$ be a family of pairwise disjoint Σ-regular sets whose union is $\theta(\Sigma)$. Then there exists a complete sequential machine, with a start state and with output symbols $E^1, \ldots, E^s$, which satisfies the following condition: For each tape $J = I_1 \ldots I_r$, the ith output E_i in the resulting output sequence $E_1 \ldots E_r$ is E^s if and only if $I_1 \ldots I_i$ is in U_s.

EXERCISE 8. Let $\Sigma = \{a\}$. Then a set U is regular if and only if $U = \{(a)^s | s \text{ in } A\}$, where A is an ultimately periodic set of non-negative integers.*

EXERCISE 9. Let U be a Σ_1-regular set. If $\Sigma_1 \subseteq \Sigma_2$ then U is Σ_2-regular. From this, infer that if U and V are Σ_3-regular and Σ_4-regular, respectively, then U and V are both regular with respect to a common alphabet.

EXERCISE 10. There exists only a denumerably infinite number of Σ-regular sets.

4.2 Nondeterministic automata. A recognition device is now introduced which is capable of having any one of many next states. This new "machine" is useful in the study of automata, particularly that aspect dealing with regular sets.

Definition 4.4. A *nondeterministic automaton* is a 5-tuple

$$A = (K, \Sigma, \delta, S_0, F),$$

where

(i) δ is a function from $K \times \Sigma$ into 2^K,
(ii) S_0 and F are subsets of K, with S_0 nonempty.

A nondeterministic automaton differs from an automaton in two ways. First, the function δ takes each state and each input into a *set* of states (possibly the empty set $\emptyset$). And second, the nondeterministic automaton has a set S_0 of "start" states. The significance of F for both devices is the same.

An automaton is a special case of a nondeterministic automaton in which S_0 and each $\delta(q, I)$ are sets of one state.

Definition 4.5. Let $A = (K, \Sigma, \delta, S_0, F)$ be a nondeterministic automaton. A tape $I_1 \ldots I_n$ is said to be *accepted* by A if there exists a sequence $s_0, \ldots, s_n$ of states such that
(i) s_0 is in S_0,
(ii) s_i is in $\delta(s_{i-1}, I_i)$ for $1 \leq i \leq n$,
(iii) s_n is in F.†
Let $T(A)$ denote the set of all tapes accepted by A.

---

* Let A be a set of non-negative integers. Let the elements of A, ordered by increasing magnitude, be $y_1, y_2, \ldots$. Then A is said to be an *ultimately periodic set of non-negative integers* if either A is finite or $y_1, y_2 - y_1, \ldots, y_{n+1} - y_n, \ldots$ is an ultimately periodic sequence. (See exercise 5 of Section 1.2.)

† It is understood that ϵ is an accepted tape if $S_0 \cap F$ is nonempty.

	I^1	I^2
q_1	$\{q_1, q_3\}$	$\{q_3\}$
q_2	$\{q_1, q_2\}$	$\{q_1, q_2, q_3\}$
q_3	$\emptyset$	$\{q_2\}$

FIGURE 4.3

EXAMPLE 1. Let $A = (K, \Sigma, \delta, \{q_1, q_2\}, \{q_2, q_3\})$, where δ is in Fig. 4.3.

(a) The tape I^1 is in $T(A)$. Pictorially, we have

$$I^1$$
$$q_1 \quad q_3$$

with q_3 in $T(A)$.

(b) Consider the tape $I^2 I^1$. The sequence q_1, q_3, $\emptyset$ obtained pictorially by

$$I^2 \quad I^1$$
$$q_1 \quad q_3 \quad \emptyset$$

does not lead to a state in F. But another sequence of states, namely q_2, q_2, q_2 obtained pictorially by

$$I^2 \quad I^1$$
$$q_2 \quad q_2 \quad q_2$$

does lead to a state in F. Thus $I^2 I^1$ is in $T(A)$.

EXERCISE 1. Let δ be given in Fig. 4.3 and

$$A = (K, \Sigma, \delta, \{q_2\}, \{q_1\}).$$

(i) Is $I^1 I^2 I^2$ in $T(A)$? (ii) Is $I^2 I^1 I^2$ in $T(A)$? (iii) Is $I^1 I^1 I^2 I^2$ in $T(A)$?

The importance of nondeterministic automata to automata theory is, as shown in Theorem 4.1, that the set of tapes accepted by a nondeterministic automaton is a regular set. Thus, measured by $T(A)$, automata are just as powerful as nondeterministic automata.

Notation. Let $A = (K, \Sigma, \delta, S_0, F)$ be a nondeterministic automaton. Denote by $D(A)$ the automaton $(L, \Sigma, \delta_{D(A)}, t_0, G)$, where $L = 2^K$, $\delta_{D(A)}$ is the function on $L \times \Sigma$ defined by $\delta_{D(A)}(y, I) = \cup_{q \text{ in } y} \delta(q, I)$, $t_0 = S_0$, and G is the family of those subsets of K containing at least one element of F.

	I^1	I^2
$\{q_1, q_2, q_3\}$	$\{q_1, q_2, q_3\}$	$\{q_1, q_2, q_3\}$
$\{q_1, q_2\}$	$\{q_1, q_2, q_3\}$	$\{q_1, q_2, q_3\}$
$\{q_1, q_3\}$	$\{q_1, q_3\}$	$\{q_2, q_3\}$
$\{q_2, q_3\}$	$\{q_1, q_2\}$	$\{q_1, q_2, q_3\}$
$\{q_1\}$	$\{q_1, q_3\}$	$\{q_3\}$
$\{q_2\}$	$\{q_1, q_2\}$	$\{q_1, q_2, q_3\}$
$\{q_3\}$	$\emptyset$	$\{q_2\}$
$\emptyset$	$\emptyset$	$\emptyset$

	I^1	I^2
q_1	$\{q_1, q_2\}$	$\{q_3\}$
q_2	$\emptyset$	$\{q_2, q_4\}$
q_3	$\{q_1, q_2, q_4\}$	$\emptyset$
q_4	$\{q_2, q_3\}$	$\{q_3\}$

FIGURE 4.4   FIGURE 4.5

EXAMPLE 2. Let A be the nondeterministic automaton defined in example 1. Then

$$D(A) = (L, \Sigma, \delta_{D(A)}, t_0, G),$$

where

$$t_0 = \{q_1, q_2\},$$

$$G = \big\{ \{q_1, q_2, q_3\}, \{q_2, q_3\}, \{q_2\}, \{q_3\}, \{q_1, q_2\}, \{q_1, q_3\} \big\},$$

and δ is given in Fig. 4.4. Observe that each element of G contains either q_2 or q_3. Typical of the function $\delta_{D(A)}$ is

$$\delta_{D(A)}(\{q_1, q_2, q_3\}, I^1) = \delta(q_1, I^1) \cup \delta(q_2, I^1) \cup \delta(q_3, I^1) = \{q_1, q_2, q_3\}.$$

EXERCISE 2. Let δ be given by Fig. 4.5. Find $D(A)$ where (i) $A = (K, \Sigma, \delta, \{q_1, q_2\}, \{q_1, q_4\})$; (ii) $A = (K, \Sigma, \delta, \{q_1, q_3\}, \{q_1, q_4\})$.

Theorem 4.1. $T(A) = T(D(A))$ for every nondeterministic automaton A.

Proof. Let $J = I_1 \ldots I_n$ be a tape in $T(A)$. Let $s_0, \ldots, s_n$ be the associated sequence of states produced by Definition 4.5. Using induction, we shall show that s_j is in $\delta_{D(A)}(t_0, I_1 \ldots I_j)$. Suppose that $j = 1$. By assumption, s_1 is in $\delta(s_0, I_1)$ and s_0 is in t_0. Thus s_1 is in $\delta_{D(A)}(t_0, I_1) = \cup_{s \text{ in } t_0} \delta(s, I_1)$. Assume the assertion is true for $j \leq k$. By definition, $\delta_{D(A)}(t_0, I_1 \ldots I_{k+1}) = \delta_{D(A)}[\delta_{D(A)}(t_0, I_1 \ldots I_k), I_{k+1}]$. By induction

s_k is in $\delta_{D(A)}(t_0, I_1 \ldots I_k)$. By the definition of $\delta_{D(A)}$,

$$\delta(s_k, I_{k+1}) \subseteq \bigcup_{y \text{ in } \delta_{D(A)}(t_0, I_1 \cdots I_k)} \delta(y, I_{k+1})$$

$$= \delta_{D(A)}[\delta_{D(A)}(t_0, I_1 \ldots I_k), I_{k+1}] = \delta_{D(A)}(t_0, I_1 \ldots I_{k+1}).$$

Since s_{k+1} is in $\delta(s_k, I_{k+1})$, s_{k+1} is in $\delta_{D(A)}(t_0, I_1 \ldots I_{k+1})$. Thus s_j is in $\delta_{D(A)}(t_0, I_1 \ldots I_j)$ for all $j \leq n$. In particular, s_n is in $\delta_{D(A)}(t_0, I_1 \ldots I_n)$ $= \delta_{D(A)}(t_0, J)$. Since s_n is in F, $\delta_{D(A)}(t_0, J)$ is in G. Thus J is in $T(D(A))$. Hence $T(A) \subseteq T(D(A))$.

Assume next that a tape $J = I_1 \ldots I_n$ is in $T(D(A))$. For each k let $t_k = \delta_{D(A)}(t_0, I_1 \ldots I_k)$. Then t_n is in G. Let s_n be any state of A which is in $t_n \cap F$. The definition of t_n being in G guarantees the existence of s_n. Since s_n is in

$$t_n = \delta_{D(A)}(t_0, I_1 \ldots I_n) = \delta_{D(A)}(t_{n-1}, I_n),$$

it follows from the definition of $\delta_{D(A)}$ that s_n is in $\delta(s_{n-1}, I_n)$ for some element s_{n-1} in t_{n-1}. Now

$$t_{n-1} = \delta_{D(A)}(t_0, I_1 \ldots I_{n-1}) = \delta_{D(A)}(t_{n-2}, I_{n-1}).$$

Thus s_{n-1} is in $\delta(s_{n-2}, I_{n-1})$ for some element s_{n-2} in t_{n-2}. Continuing in this way, we obtain a sequence $s_n, s_{n-1}, \ldots, s_0$ such that s_k is in t_k for each k, s_k is in $\delta(s_{k-1}, I_k)$ for $k > 0$, and s_n is in F. Since $t_0 = S_0$, we see that s_0 is in S_0. Therefore J is in $T(A)$. Thus $T(D(A)) \subseteq T(A)$.

Since $T(A) \subseteq T(D(A))$ and $T(D(A)) \subseteq T(A)$, it follows that $T(A) = T(D(A))$.

Theorem 4.1 is important as a theoretical tool enabling us to prove facts about regular sets. Among other places, it is used in the proof of the basic Theorem 4.2.

EXERCISE 3.   Let $S = (K_S, \Sigma, \Delta, \delta_S, \lambda_S)$ be a complete sequential machine with a start state q_1. Let $A = (K_A, \Sigma, \delta_A, p_1, F)$ be any automaton and $U = T(A)$.

(a) Consider the automaton $C = (K_A \times K_S, \Sigma, \delta_C, (p_1, q_1), F \times K_S)$, where $\delta_C[(p, q), I] = [\delta_A(p, I), \delta_S(q, I)]$ for each I in Σ. Show that $U = T(C)$.

(b) Let H be the nondeterministic automaton

$$H = (K_A \times K_S, \Delta, \delta_H, (p_1, q_1), F \times K_S),$$

where for each element E in Δ,

$$\delta_H[(p, q), E]$$
$$= \{(p', q') | \lambda_S(q, I) = E \text{ and } \delta_C[(p, q), I] = (p', q') \text{ for some } I \text{ in } \Sigma\}.$$

Show that $T(H) = \{\lambda_S(q, J)|J \text{ in } U\}$. In less precise language, this means that a complete sequential machine maps a regular set into a regular set.

EXERCISE 4. Let V be a Σ-regular set. For each element x of Σ let $h(x)$ be a Σ-regular set. Let $h(\epsilon) = \epsilon$. Prove that

$$\bigcup_{\substack{w \text{ in } V \\ w = x_1 \cdots x_r}} h(x_1) \ldots h(x_r)$$

is Σ-regular.

EXERCISE 5. Let J be a tape and U a regular set. Show that the set of those tapes in U which do not contain J is regular. [*Hint:* Use exercises 3 and 4.]

4.3 Characterization theorems. We now consider regular sets in greater detail. In particular, we shall characterize the family of Σ-regular sets as well as an arbitrary Σ-regular set.

Definition 4.6. Let C and D be sets of tapes. The (*complex*) *product* CD is the set of those tapes XY for which X is in C and Y is in D.

EXAMPLE 1. Let $C = \{I^1I^1, I^2I^1\}$ and $D = \{I^1, I^3I^2, I^1I^2\}$. Then

$$CD = \{I^1I^1I^1, I^1I^1I^3I^2, I^1I^1I^1I^2, I^2I^1I^1, I^2I^1I^3I^2, I^2I^1I^1I^2\}.$$

Note that CD does not coincide with DC.

Definition 4.7. Let C be a set of tapes. The *star* of C, written C^*, is the set of tapes $C^* = \bigcup_0^\infty C^i$, where $C^0 = \epsilon$ and $C^{i+1} = C^iC$ for each $i \geq 0$.

EXAMPLE 2. Let $C = \{I^1, I^2I^3\}$. Then

$$C^* = \{I^1, I^2I^3, I^1I^2I^3, I^2I^3I^1, I^1I^1, I^2I^3I^2I^3, \ldots\}.$$

EXERCISE 1. Let P be a family of subsets of $\theta(\Sigma)$, containing the finite sets, which is closed under the operations of union, product, and star. Let Q be the class of all such families P. Show that the family of sets $\cap_{P \text{ in } Q} P$ is in Q. This family is called the *smallest* family of subsets of θ, containing the finite sets, which is closed under the operations of union, product, and star.

A characterization of the family of regular sets involving union, product, and star is now given. It uses the terminology of the above exercise.

Theorem 4.2. The family of Σ-regular sets is the smallest family of subsets of θ, containing the finite sets, which is closed under the operations of union, product, and star.

Proof. Let Γ_1 be the family of Σ-regular sets. Let Γ_2 be the smallest family of subsets of θ, containing the finite sets, which is closed under the operations of union, product, and star. We shall prove that $\Gamma_1 = \Gamma_2$ by showing that $\Gamma_2 \subseteq \Gamma_1$ and $\Gamma_1 \subseteq \Gamma_2$.

(a) $\Gamma_2 \subseteq \Gamma_1$. To see this it suffices to show each of the following:

(i) $\emptyset$ and each set $\{J\}$ consisting of one tape are in Γ_1.

(ii) If U and V are in Γ_1, then $U \cup V$ and UV are in Γ_1.

(iii) If U is in Γ_1, then U^* is in Γ_1.

Then Γ_1 is a family of subsets of θ, containing the finite sets, which is closed under the operations of union, product, and star. Since Γ_2 is a subfamily of each such family, the desired inclusion relation follows.

As to (i), clearly $\emptyset$ and $\{\epsilon\}$ are in Γ_1. Let $J = I_1 \ldots I_k$ be any tape. Let $K = \{q_i | 1 \le i \le k + 2\}$ be a set of $k + 2$ abstract symbols. Let $A = (K, \Sigma, \delta, q_1, \{q_{k+1}\})$, where the function δ is defined by $\delta(q_i, I_i) = q_{i+1}$, $\delta(q_i, I) = q_{k+2}$ for I in $\Sigma - \{I_i\}$, $1 \le i \le k$, and $\delta = q_{k+2}$ otherwise. Then $T(A) = \{J\}$.

As to (ii) let $U = T(A)$ and $V = T(B)$, where $A = (K_A, \Sigma, \delta_A, s_0^A, F_A)$ and $B = (K_B, \Sigma, \delta_B, s_0^B, F_B)$. Let C be the automaton

$$\left(K_A \times K_B, \Sigma, \delta_C, (s_0^A, s_0^B), (F_A \times K_B) \cup (K_A \times F_B)\right),$$

where $\delta_C((p, q), I) = \left(\delta_A(p, I), \delta_B(q, I)\right)$ for each p in K_A, q in K_B, and I in Σ. A tape J is in $T(C)$ if and only if $\delta_C((s_0^A, s_0^B), J) = (\delta_A(s_0^A, J), \delta_B(s_0^B, J))$ is in $(F_A \times K_B) \cup (K_A \times F_B)$. This is equivalent to either $\delta_A(s_0^A, J)$ being in F_A or $\delta_B(s_0^B, J)$ being in F_B, that is, J being in $U \cup V$. Thus $T(C) = U \cup V$. To see that UV is regular, we shall assume, without loss of generality, that $K_A \cap K_B = \emptyset$. Let D be the nondeterministic automaton $D = (K_A \cup K_B, \Sigma, \delta_D, \{s_0^A\}, F_B)$, where the function δ_D is defined as follows:

$$\delta_D(q, I) = \{\delta_A(q, I)\} \qquad \text{if} \quad q \text{ is in } K_A - F_A,$$

$$\delta_D(q, I) = \{\delta_A(q, I), \delta_B(s_0^B, I)\} \qquad \text{if} \quad q \text{ is in } F_A,$$

and

$$\delta_D(q, I) = \{\delta_B(q, I)\} \qquad \text{if} \quad q \text{ is in } K_B.$$

A tape J is in UV if and only if $J = J_1 J_2$, for some J_1 in U and J_2 in V. This is equivalent to $\delta_A(s_0^A, J_1)$ being in F_A and $\delta_B(s_0^B, J_2)$ being in F_B, which is equivalent to $J_1 J_2$ being in $T(D)$. Thus $UV = T(D)$.

As to (iii) let $U = T(A)$, where $A = (K, \Sigma, \delta_A, s_0, F)$. Let B be the nondeterministic automaton $B = (K, \Sigma, \delta_B, \{s_0\}, F)$, where δ_B is the function defined by

$$\delta_B(q, I) = \{\delta_A(q, I)\} \qquad \text{if} \quad q \text{ is in } K - F$$

and

$$\delta_B(q, I) = \{\delta_A(q, I), \delta_A(s_0, I)\} \qquad \text{if} \quad q \text{ is in } F.$$

It is left as an exercise to verify that $U^* = T(B)$.

(b) $\Gamma_1 \subseteq \Gamma_2$. To see this, let U be any regular set. We shall show that U is obtained from certain finite subsets of θ, using the operations of union, product, and star a finite number of times. From this it will follow that Γ_1 is a subfamily of each family of subsets of θ, containing the finite sets, which is closed under the operations of union, product, and star; thus $\Gamma_1 \subseteq \Gamma_2$. Since U is regular, $U = T(A)$ for some automaton $A = (K, \Sigma, \delta, q_1, F)$. Denote the states of A by $q_1, \ldots, q_n$. Suppose that α_{ij}^u has been defined for $0 \leq u \leq k - 1 < n$ and $1 \leq i, j \leq n$. Suppose further that

(i) α_{ij}^u is the set of those tapes $I_1 \ldots I_r$ for which $\delta(q_i, I_1 \ldots I_r) = q_j$ and for each $1 \leq t < r$, if $\delta(q_i, I_1 \ldots I_t) = q_q$, then $x \leq u$. In particular,

(ii) α_{ij}^0 is the set of those tapes J, of length at most 1, for which $\delta(q_i, J) = q_j$.

Thus (i) is true for $k = 1$. For $1 \leq i, j \leq n$ define α_{ij}^k to be the set

$$\text{(iii)} \quad \alpha_{ij}^k = \alpha_{ij}^{k-1} \cup \alpha_{ik}^{k-1}(\alpha_{kk}^{k-1})^*\alpha_{kj}^{k-1}.$$

By (i) and inspection it is seen that each tape in the set on the right side of (iii) takes q_i to q_j, with all intermediate states q_x such that $x \leq k$. Let $I_1 \ldots I_r$ be any tape taking q_i to q_j, with all intermediate states q_x such that $x \leq k$. If all intermediate states q_x are such that $x \leq k - 1$, then $I_1 \ldots I_r$ is in α_{ij}^{k-1}. If there are intermediate states q_x such that $x = k$, then $I_1 \ldots I_r$ is in $\alpha_{ik}^{k-1}(\alpha_{kk}^{k-1})^*\alpha_{kj}^{k-1}$. Thus α_{ij}^k satisfies (i). In this way, α_{ij}^k becomes defined for $0 \leq k \leq n$ and $1 \leq i, j \leq n$, and satisfies (i).

Let $q_{m(1)}, \ldots, q_{m(v)}$ be the different states in F. By (i), each $\alpha_{1m(i)}^n$ is the set of tapes taking q_1 to $q_{m(i)}$, with no intermediate state q_x such that $x > n$. Since there is no state q_j for which $j > n$, then $\alpha_{1m(i)}^n$ is the set of tapes taking q_1 to $q_{m(i)}$. Therefore $U = T(A) = \cup_i \alpha_{1m(i)}^n$. Now each α_{ij}^0 is a finite set, and each α_{ij}^k is obtained from sets of the form α_{yz}^{k-1} by union, product, and star. Therefore U is obtained from finite sets by union, product, and star. Thus U is in Γ_2, that is, $\Gamma_1 \subseteq \Gamma_2$.

In effect Theorem 4.2 asserts that each regular set is obtained from a finite number of finite sets of tapes by using the operations of union, product, and star a finite number of times. The proof of part (b) provides an algorithm for determining the regular set defined by an automaton. The algorithm consists in constructing the various sets α_{ij}^k [there are $n^2(n+1)$ of these] and then taking an appropriate set union. While this method is straightforward, it is quite lengthy and tedious. It would be desirable to have a more efficient method.

Unsolved problem. Find a more efficient method for calculating $T(A)$ given A.

EXAMPLE 3. Consider the automaton $A = (K, \Sigma, \delta, q_1, \{q_1\})$, where δ is shown in Fig. 4.6. Let us use the algorithm of part (b) of Theorem 4.2 to determine $T(A)$. The appropriate α_{ij}^k are as follows:

	I^1	I^2
q_1	q_2	q_1
q_2	q_1	q_1

FIGURE 4.6

$$\alpha_{11}^0 = \{I^2, \epsilon\},$$

$$\alpha_{12}^0 = \{I^1\},$$

$$\alpha_{21}^0 = \{I^1, I^2\},$$

$$\alpha_{22}^0 = \{\epsilon\},$$

$$\alpha_{11}^1 = \alpha_{11}^0 \cup \alpha_{11}^0(\alpha_{11}^0)^*\alpha_{11}^0 = \{I^2, \epsilon\} \cup \{I^2, \epsilon\}\{I^2, \epsilon\}^*\{I^2, \epsilon\},$$

$$\alpha_{12}^1 = \alpha_{12}^0 \cup \alpha_{11}^0(\alpha_{11}^0)^*\alpha_{12}^0 = \{I^1\} \cup \{I^2, \epsilon\}\{I^2, \epsilon\}^*I^1,$$

$$\alpha_{21}^1 = \alpha_{21}^0 \cup \alpha_{21}^0(\alpha_{11}^0)^*\alpha_{11}^0 = \{I^1, I^2\} \cup \{I^1, I^2\}\{I^2, \epsilon\}^*\{I^2, \epsilon\},$$

$$\alpha_{22}^1 = \alpha_{22}^0 \cup \alpha_{21}^0(\alpha_{11}^0)^*\alpha_{12}^0 = \{\epsilon\} \cup \{I^1, I^2\}\{I^2, \epsilon\}^*I .$$

Then

$$T(A) = \alpha_{11}^2 = \alpha_{11}^1 \cup \alpha_{12}^1(\alpha_{22}^1)^*\alpha_{21}^1.$$

After substitution for the α_{jk}^1, the expression for $T(A)$ becomes rather complicated. The end result can be simplified, but that is a matter we shall not discuss.

Unsolved problem. Develop an efficient calculus for handling expressions involving star, product, and union. For example, $\epsilon + AA^* = A^*$.

Suppose that $A = (K, \Sigma, \delta, s_0, F)$ and $U = T(A)$. Then $\theta(\Sigma) - T(A) = T(B)$, where $B = (K, \Sigma, \delta, s_0, K - F)$. Thus the family of Σ-regular sets is closed under the operation of complementation. Since the empty set $\emptyset$ is regular and the union of two regular sets is regular, we have the following corollary.

Corollary. The family of Σ-regular sets is a Boolean algebra of sets.

EXERCISE 2. Prove that $U^* = T(B)$ in (iii), part (a) of Theorem 4.2.

EXERCISE 3. Simplify $T(A)$ in example 3.

EXERCISE 4. By the Corollary to Theorem 4.2, the intersection of two regular sets is regular. Show this fact directly as follows: Let $U = T(A)$ and $V = T(B)$, where

$$A = (K_A, \Sigma, \delta_A, s_0^A, F_A) \quad \text{and} \quad B = (K_B, \Sigma, \delta_B, s_0^B, F_B).$$

Let $C = (K_A \times K_B, \Sigma, \delta_C, (s_0^A, s_0^B), F_A \times F_B)$, where $\delta_C[(p, q), I] = [\delta_A(p, I), \delta_B(q, I)]$ for each p in K_A, q in K_B, and I in Σ. Then $U \cap V = T(C)$.

Theorem 4.2 characterizes the family of regular sets. But it says nothing about determining whether or not a particular set is regular. We now characterize a regular set in several ways.

Theorem 4.3. The following three conditions about a set U of tapes are equivalent:
   (i) U is a regular set.
   (ii) U is the union of some equivalence classes generated by a congruence relation, of finite index, on $\theta(\Sigma)$.
   (iii) The congruence relation $\equiv$ next defined on $\theta(\Sigma)$ is of finite index. $X \equiv Y$ if and only if for all tapes Z and W, ZXW being in U is equivalent to ZYW being in U.

Proof. It is sufficient to show that (i) implies (ii), (ii) implies (iii), and (iii) implies (i).

Suppose that (i) holds. Let $U = T(A)$ for some automaton $A = (K, \Sigma, \delta, s_0, F)$. Let $\approx$ be the relation defined on $\theta(\Sigma)$ thus. $X \approx Y$ holds if and only if $\delta(p, X) = \delta(p, Y)$ for all states p in A. Clearly $\approx$ is an equivalence relation. To see that $\approx$ is right invariant, suppose that $X \approx Y$ holds. For any tape Z

$$\delta(p, XZ) = \delta[\delta(p, X), Z]$$
$$= \delta[\delta(p, Y), Z] \quad \text{(as } X \approx Y \text{ holds)}$$
$$= \delta(p, YZ).$$

To see that $\approx$ is left invariant,

$$\delta(p, ZX) = \delta[\delta(p, Z), X]$$
$$= \delta[\delta(p, Z), Y] \quad \text{(as } X \approx Y \text{ holds)}$$
$$= \delta(p, ZY).$$

Thus $\approx$ is both right and left invariant, i.e., is a congruence relation.

Let $r = \#(K)$. Then there are r^r distinct functions of K into K. For each tape X the function f_X, defined by $f_X(q) = \delta(q, X)$, is one of these

r^r functions. Thus there are at most r^r different functions f_X. Hence there are at most r^r different equivalence classes. Therefore $\approx$ is of finite index.

Suppose that X is in $T(A)$ and that $X \approx Y$ holds. Then $\delta(s_0, X) = \delta(s_0, Y)$, so that Y is in $T(A)$. Thus the equivalence class $[X]$ is a subset of $T(A)$. Then $U = T(A) = \bigcup_{X \text{ in } T(A)} [X]$. Therefore U is the union of some equivalence classes generated by $\approx$. Thus (i) implies (ii).

Now suppose that (ii) holds. Let $\approx$ be a congruence relation satisfying (ii). Let $\equiv$ be the relation defined by (iii). Obviously $\equiv$ is symmetric, transitive, reflexive, left invariant, and right invariant. Therefore $\equiv$ is a congruence relation. It remains to show that $\equiv$ is of finite index. To see this, let X and Y be any tapes such that $X \approx Y$ holds. Suppose that ZXW is in U. Since $\approx$ is both left and right invariant, $ZXW \approx ZYW$. As U is the union of equivalence classes generated by $\approx$, ZYW is in U. Similarly ZYW being in U implies that ZXW is in U. Hence if $X \approx Y$ holds, then $X \equiv Y$. Thus each equivalence class generated by $\approx$ is a subset of some equivalence class generated by $\equiv$. Then the number of equivalence classes generated by $\equiv$ is at most the number of equivalence classes generated by $\approx$. Since $\approx$ generates only a finite number of equivalence classes, being of finite index, so does $\equiv$. Therefore $\equiv$ is of finite index.

Finally, suppose that (iii) holds. We shall define an automaton $A = (K, \Sigma, \delta, s_0, F)$ for which $U = T(A)$. Let K be the set of equivalence classes generated by the congruence relation $\equiv$. By hypothesis, K is finite. Let D be any equivalence class and X an element in D. Define $\delta(D, I)$ to be $[XI]$ for each I in Σ. Let Y be any other tape in D. Then $X \equiv Y$. Since $\equiv$ is right invariant, $XI \equiv YI$. Therefore $[XI] = [YI]$. Thus $\delta(D, I)$ is uniquely defined, that is, is independent of which element X in D is selected. Let $s_0 = [\epsilon]$ and $F = \{[X] \mid X \text{ in } U\}$. From the definition of $\equiv$, if X is in U and $Y \equiv X$, then Y is in U. Thus $U = \bigcup_{X \text{ in } U} [X]$. Then $\delta(s_0, X) = [X]$ is in F if and only if X is in U. Consequently, $U = T(A)$. Thus (iii) implies (i).

We now illustrate the proof of Theorem 4.3 for a particular regular set U. In the process we shall exhibit the resulting congruence relations $\approx$ and $\equiv$, and the automaton produced by (iii).

EXAMPLE 4. Let A be the automaton $A = (K, \Sigma, \delta, p_1, \{p_2, p_3\})$, where δ is shown in Fig. 4.7. Then

$$U = T(A) = \{(I^2)^n I^1 X \mid n \geq 0, \text{all } X\}.$$

The congruence relation $\approx$ of (ii) is defined by $X \approx Y$ if and only if $\delta(q, X) = \delta(q, Y)$ for all states q. The equivalence classes generated by $\approx$ are

$$J_1 = [\epsilon], \qquad J_2 = [I^1], \qquad \text{and} \qquad J_3 = [I^1 I^1].$$

	I^1	I^2
p_1	p_2	p_1
p_2	p_3	p_2
p_3	p_2	p_3

FIGURE 4.7

	I^1	I^2
J_1	$J_2 \cup J_3$	J_1
$J_2 \cup J_3$	$J_2 \cup J_3$	$J_2 \cup J_3$

FIGURE 4.8

For each tape X in J_1 we see that $\delta(p_1, X) = p_1$, $\delta(p_2, X) = p_2$, and $\delta(p_3, X) = p_3$. For each tape X in J_2 we see that $\delta(p_1, X) = p_2$, $\delta(p_2, X) = p_3$, and $\delta(p_3, X) = p_2$. For each tape X in J_3 we see that $\delta(p_1, X) = p_3$, $\delta(p_2, X) = p_2$, and $\delta(p_3, X) = p_3$. Clearly $U = J_2 \cup J_3$.

The congruence relation $\equiv$ generated by U and $\approx$ of (ii) is as follows. For tapes X and Y in the same J_i, $i = 1, 2, 3$, $X \equiv Y$. For X in J_2 and Y in J_3, $X \equiv Y$. For X in J_1 and Y in J_2, $X \not\equiv Y$. For X in J_1 and Y in J_3, $X \not\equiv Y$. There are two equivalence classes generated by $\equiv$, namely $J_2 \cup J_3$ and J_1. This is in agreement with the general theory which asserts that each equivalence class generated by $\approx$ is a subset of an equivalence class generated by $\equiv$.

The automaton $B = (K_B, \Sigma, \delta_B, s_0, F)$ produced from U by (iii) is as follows. K_B has two states, J_1 and $J_2 \cup J_3$; $s_0 = J_1$; and $F = \{J_2 \cup J_3\}$. δ_B is given in Fig. 4.8. Then $U = T(B)$. Observe that if we start with an automaton A, execute (ii), then (iii), and finally (i), we do not always return to the automaton A.

Another characterization for a set U to be regular is now given. It is quite similar to Theorem 4.3.

Theorem 4.4. The following three conditions about a set U of tapes are equivalent:

   (i) U is a regular set.
   (ii) U is the union of some of the equivalence classes of a right invariant equivalence relation, of finite index, on $\theta(\Sigma)$.
   (iii) The right invariant equivalence relation $\sim$ next defined on $\theta(\Sigma)$ is of finite index. $X \sim Y$ if and only if for each tape W, XW being in U is equivalent to YW being in U.

The proof of Theorem 4.4 is almost identical with that of Theorem 4.3. The relation $\approx$ in the proof of (i) implies (ii) may be defined more simply as follows. $X \approx Y$ holds if and only if $\delta(s_0, X) = \delta(s_0, Y)$. The proof is left as an exercise.

By exercise 10, Section 4.1, there exists only a denumerably infinite number of Σ-regular sets. Now we have a denumerably infinite number of tapes. It is an elementary fact from set theory that the number of sets of tapes is nondenumerable [S2]. Thus there exists a nondenumerable number of sets which are not regular. Using Theorem 4.3, we exhibit a specific set which is not regular.

EXAMPLE 5. Let $\Sigma = \{a, b\}$. Consider the set $U = \{(a)^n(b)^n | n \geq 1\}$. Suppose that U is a regular set. Let $\approx$ be a congruence relation satisfying (ii) of Theorem 4.3. Since $\approx$ is of finite index, all the elements $(a)^i$, $i \geq 1$, cannot be nonequivalent. Thus, for some m and n, $m \neq n$, $(a)^m \approx (a)^n$. As $\approx$ is right invariant, $(a)^m(b)^m \approx (a)^n(b)^m$. Since U is the union of equivalence classes and U contains $(a)^m(b)^m$, U contains $(a)^n(b)^m$. This is a contradiction. Thus U is not regular.

EXERCISE 5. Let U be the regular set $\{(ab)^n | n \geq 1\}$. Find the two equivalence relations $\approx$ and $\equiv$ of Theorem 4.3. Using $\equiv$, find an automaton A so that $U = T(A)$.

EXERCISE 6. Prove Theorem 4.4.

EXERCISE 7. Show that each of the following sets is not regular ($\Sigma = \{a, b\}$).
    (a) $U = \{(a)^n b(a)^n | n \geq 1\}$.
    (b) $U = \{(a)^n | n \text{ a prime integer}\}$.
    (c) The set of all tapes with exactly as many a's as b's.
    (d) The set of all tapes with more a's than b's.
    (e) $U = \{(ab)^{n^2} | n \geq 1\}$.

EXERCISE 8. If U is a regular set, show that the number of equivalence classes generated by $\sim$ of Theorem 4.4 is the least number of states of an automaton defining U.

EXERCISE 9. For each tape $J = J_1 \ldots I_n$ let $J^R = I_n I_{n-1} \ldots I_1$. Let $\epsilon^R = \epsilon$. If U is a set of tapes, denote by U^R the set $U^R = \{X^R | X \text{ in } U\}$. Show each of the following:
    (a) $(XY)^R = Y^R X^R$.
    (b) If U is regular, then so is U^R. [*Hint:* Use (iii) of Theorem 4.3.]

EXERCISE 10. Let $A = (K, \Sigma, \delta, S_0, F)$ be a nondeterministic automaton. The *dual* A^D of A is defined as the nondeterministic automaton $A^D = (K, \Sigma, \delta^D, F, S_0)$, where δ^D is the function satisfying the condition

$$p \text{ is in } \delta^D(q, I) \text{ if and only if } q \text{ is in } \delta(p, I).$$

Show that $T(A^D) = T(A)^R$ for each nondeterministic automaton A.

EXERCISE 11. Let $\Sigma = \{a, b, c\}$ and let A be an infinite subset of $\theta(\{a, b\})$. For each tape w in L, let B_w be a nonempty subset of $\theta(\{a, b\})$

such that $B_{w_1} \cap B_{w_2} = \emptyset$ for $w_1 \neq w_2$. Prove that $\underset{w \text{ in } A}{\bigcup} wcB_w$ is not a regular set. In particular, this shows that $\{wcw | w \text{ in } A\}$ and $\{wcw^R | w \text{ in } A\}$ are not regular sets.

EXERCISE 12. Prove Theorem 4.4 with "right invariant," "XW" and "YW," replaced by "left invariant," "WX" and "WY," respectively. [*Hint:* Use Theorem 4.4 and exercise 9.]

4.4 Equivalence of automata. Two complete sequential machines are called equivalent if both do the same work. Since work for complete sequential machines is regarded as input sequences versus output sequences, the definition of equivalence is formulated accordingly. In the same spirit, two automata are deemed equivalent if both do the same work. Since work for an automaton is regarded as its ability to discriminate in recognizing tapes we have the following:

Definition 4.8. Two automata A and B are called *equivalent* if $T(A) = T(B)$.

There is a finite procedure for determining if two automata A and B are equivalent. The procedure (Theorem 4.5) consists of verifying that $T(A)$ and $T(B)$ coincide for all tapes up to a certain length [depending on $\#(K_A)$ and $\#(K_B)$], that is, verifying that each tape J up to a certain length is in $T(A)$ if and only if J is in $T(B)$.

Theorem 4.5. Let A and B be automata with m and n states, respectively. Let $\Sigma_A = \Sigma_B$. If $T(A)$ and $T(B)$ coincide for all tapes up to length $m + n - 2$, then $T(A) = T(B)$. Furthermore, $m + n - 2$ is the smallest possible number in the general case.

Proof. Let $A = (K_A, \Sigma, \delta_A, p_1, F_A)$ and $B = (K_B, \Sigma, \delta_B, q_1, F_B)$. For each I in Σ and q in K_X, $X = A, B$, let $\lambda_X(q, I) = 1$ if q is in F_X, and $\lambda_X(q, I) = 0$ otherwise. Consider the complete sequential machines $S = (K_A, \Sigma, \{0, 1\}, \delta_A, \lambda_A)$ and $T = (K_B, \Sigma, \{0, 1\}, \delta_B, \lambda_B)$. Suppose that $T(A)$ and $T(B)$ coincide for all tapes up to length $m + n - 2$. Then, as is easily seen, $p_1 \overset{m+n-1}{\equiv} q_1$. By Theorem 1.2, $p_1 \equiv q_1$. Thus $T(A)$ and $T(B)$ coincide for all tapes whose length is at least $m + n - 1$. Therefore $T(A) = T(B)$.

Now let m and n be positive integers. Let S and T be the complete sequential machines used in the proof of Theorem 1.2 for m and n states, respectively (Figs. 1.16, 1.17, 1.18, 1.19). Let $A = (K_S, \Sigma_S, \delta_S, p_1, \{p_1\})$ and $B = (K_T, \Sigma_T, \delta_T, q_1, \{q_1\})$. It is readily seen that $T(A) \neq T(B)$, although $T(A)$ and $T(B)$ coincide for all tapes of length up to $m + n - 3$.†

---

† The remainder of this section may be omitted on a first reading.

In automata theory, one is occasionally interested in not permitting ϵ to be a tape.† This necessitates defining A^* as $\cup_1^\infty A^i$ and frequently results in more complicated expressions. However, practically all theorems true for regular sets with ϵ are true for regular sets without ϵ, although some of the expressions and numbers are changed slightly. To illustrate, we shall prove the companion result to Theorem 4.5 when ϵ is not permitted as a tape. To indicate that we are not allowing ϵ as a tape, we shall use the term "non ϵ-automaton" instead of "automaton."

Lemma 4.1. Let S and T be complete sequential machines with m and n states, respectively. Let p_1 in S and q_1 in T be nonequivalent states. If $p_1 \stackrel{m+n-2}{\equiv} q_1$ and if $J = I_1 \ldots I_{m+n-1}$ is a tape of length $m + n - 1$ such that $\lambda_S(p_1, J) \neq \lambda_T(q_1, J)$, then S and T are both distinguished. Furthermore, for each state $r \neq p_1$ in S and each state $t \neq q_1$ in T,

$$r = \delta_S(p_1, I_1 \ldots I_i) \qquad \text{for some } i < m,$$

and

$$t = \delta_T(q_1, I_1 \ldots I_j) \qquad \text{for some } j < n.$$

Proof. Suppose that S is not distinguished. Let U be the distinguished machine equivalent to S guaranteed by Theorem 1.3. Let z_1 be the state in U which is equivalent to p_1. Then $z_1 \stackrel{m+n-2}{\equiv} q_1$. Since $\#(K_U) < m$, then $z_1 \equiv q_1$ by Theorem 1.2. Thus $p_1 \equiv q_1$, a contradiction. Therefore S is distinguished. Similarly, T is distinguished.

For us to see the second part of the conclusion, it is sufficient to verify it for machine S. Therefore, suppose it is false for S. For each i, $1 \leq i \leq m + n - 1$, let $p_{i+1} = \delta(p_1, I_1 \ldots I_i)$ and $q_{i+1} = \delta(q_1, I_1 \ldots I_i)$. Two cases arise.

(a) There exists i, $1 \leq i < m$, such that $p_1 = p_{i+1}$. Since $p_1 \stackrel{m+n-2}{\equiv} q_1$, then $p_1 = p_{i+1} \stackrel{m+n-2-i}{\equiv} q_{i+1}$ and $p_1 \stackrel{m+n-2-i}{\equiv} q_1$. Thus $q_1 \stackrel{m+n-2-i}{\equiv} q_{i+1}$. Since $i < m$, then $q_1 \stackrel{n-1+k}{\equiv} q_{i+1}$ for some $k \geq 0$. Therefore $q_1 \stackrel{n-1}{\equiv} q_{i+1}$. By Theorem 1.1, $q_1 \equiv q_{i+1}$. Then $p_{i+1} = p_1 \stackrel{m+n-2}{\equiv} q_1 \equiv q_{i+1}$. Thus

$$\lambda(p_{i+1}, I_{i+1} \ldots I_{m+n-1}) = \lambda(q_{i+1}, I_{i+1} \ldots I_{m+n-1}).$$

Clearly

$$\lambda(p_1, I_1 \ldots I_i) = \lambda(q_1, I_1 \ldots I_i).$$

Then

$$\lambda(p_1, J) = \lambda(p_1, I_1 \ldots I_i)\lambda(p_{i+1}, I_{i+1} \ldots I_{n+m-1})$$
$$= \lambda(q_1, I_1 \ldots I_i)\lambda(q_{i+1}, I_{i+1} \ldots I_{n+m-1})$$
$$= \lambda(q_1, J),$$

which is a contradiction.

---

† A specific instance of this is in Section 4.5.

(b) There is no i, $1 \leq i < m$, such that $p_1 = p_{i+1}$. Then each of the states p_i, $2 \leq i \leq m$, is in $K_S - \{p_1, r\}$. There exist i and j, $1 \leq i < j < m$, such that $p_{i+1} = p_{j+1}$. Since $p_1 \overset{m+n-2}{\equiv} q_1$, then

$$p_{i+1} \overset{m+n-2-i}{\equiv} q_{i+1} \quad \text{and} \quad p_{j+1} \overset{m+n-2-j}{\equiv} q_{j+1}.$$

Hence $q_{i+1} \overset{m+n-2-j}{\equiv} q_{j+1}$; thus $q_{i+1} \overset{n-1}{\equiv} q_{j+1}$. Thus $q_{i+1} \equiv q_{j+1}$. Then

$$p_{j+1} = p_{i+1} \overset{m+n-2-i}{\equiv} q_{i+1} \equiv q_{j+1}.$$

Therefore

$$\lambda(p_{j+1}, I_{j+1} \ldots I_{n+m-1}) = \lambda(q_{j+1}, I_{j+1} \ldots I_{n+m-1}).$$

Clearly $\lambda(p_1, I_1 \ldots I_j) = \lambda(q_1, I_1 \ldots I_j)$. Then

$$\lambda(p_1, J) = \lambda(p_1, I_1 \ldots I_j)\lambda(p_{j+1}, I_{j+1} \ldots I_{n+m-1})$$

$$= \lambda(q_1, I_1 \ldots I_j)\lambda(q_{j+1}, I_{j+1} \ldots I_{n+m-1})$$

$$= \lambda(q_1, J),$$

a contradiction.

In either case, a contradiction arises. Thus the conclusion of the lemma is true.

Notation. Let A and B be non ϵ-automata, with $\Sigma_A = \Sigma_B = \Sigma$. For states p in A and q in B, $p \sim q$ means that for each tape J, $\delta_A(p, J)$ is in F_A if and only if $\delta_B(q, J)$ is in F_B. $p \overset{k}{\sim} q$ means that for each tape J of length not greater than k, $\delta_A(p, J)$ is in F_A if and only if $\delta_B(q, J)$ is in F_B.

Lemma 4.2. Let A and B be non ϵ-automata, with $\Sigma_A = \Sigma_B = \Sigma$. For each I in Σ and q in K_X, $X = A, B$, let $\lambda_X(q, I) = 1$ if q is in F_X and $\lambda_X(q, I) = 0$ otherwise. Then for states p in A and q in B,
     (a) $p \sim q$ if and only if $\delta_A(p, I) \equiv \delta_B(q, I)$ for each I in Σ;
     (b) $p \overset{k}{\sim} q$ if and only if $\delta_A(p, I) \overset{k}{\equiv} \delta_B(q, I)$ for each I in Σ;
     (c) if $k > 1$, $p \overset{k}{\sim} q$, and J is a tape of length $i < k$, then

$$\delta_A(p, J) \overset{k-i}{\sim} \delta_B(q, J).$$

The proof is left as an exercise.

Theorem 4.6. Let A and B be non ϵ-automata with m and n states, respectively. Let p be a state in A and q a state in B.
     (a) If $p \overset{m+n-1}{\sim} q$, then $p \sim q$.
     (b) If $m = n > 1$ and $p \overset{m+n-2}{\sim} q$, then $p \sim q$.

(c) If $m \neq n$, then $m + n - 1$ is the smallest possible number in the general case. If $m = n > 1$, then $m + n - 2$ is the smallest possible number in the general case.

Proof. Let $S = (K_A, \Sigma_A, \{0, 1\}, \delta_A, \lambda_S)$ be the complete sequential machine where, for each q in K_A and I in Σ_A, $\lambda_S(q, I) = 1$ if and only if q is in F_A. Let $T = (K_B, \Sigma_B, \{0, 1\}, \delta_B, \lambda_T)$ be the complete sequential machine where, for each q in K_B and I in Σ_B, $\lambda_T(q, I) = 1$ if and only if q is in F_B.

Suppose that $p \overset{m+n-1}{\sim} q$. By Lemma 4.2, $\delta(p, I) \overset{m+n-1}{\sim} \delta(q, I)$ for each I in Σ. By Theorem 1.2, $\delta(p, I) \equiv \delta(q, I)$ for each I in Σ. Thus $p \sim q$.

Suppose that A and B each have $n > 1$ states and that $p \overset{2n-2}{\sim} q$. Assume that $p \sim q$ is false. Then $p \overset{2n-1}{\sim} q$ is false. Thus there exists a tape $J = I_1 \ldots I_{2n-1}$ of length $2n - 1$ such that $\delta(p, J)$ is in F_A and $\delta(q, J)$ is not in F_B, or $\delta(p, J)$ is not in F_A and $\delta(q, J)$ is in F_B. For each i, $i \leq 2n - 1$, let $p_i = \delta(p, I_1 \ldots I_i)$ and $q_i = \delta(q, I_1 \ldots I_i)$. Since $p \overset{2n-2}{\sim} q$, by Lemma 4.2, $p_1 = \delta(p, I_1) \overset{2n-2}{\equiv} \delta(q, I_1) = q_1$. Let $M = I_2 \ldots I_{2-1}$. From the definition of J, λ_S, and λ_T, for each element I in Σ, $\lambda_S(p_1, MI) \neq \lambda_T(q_1, MI)$. By Lemma 4.1, (i) S and T are both distinguished machines, (ii) the set $\{p_1, \ldots, p_n\}$ contains each state in S, and (iii) the set $\{q_1, \ldots, q_n\}$ contains each state in T.

We shall now show that $p = p_n$ and $q = q_n$. Since $p_1 \overset{2n-2}{\equiv} q_1$ and $n > 1$, it will follow that

$$\lambda(p, I) = \lambda(p_n, I) = \lambda(q_n, I) = \lambda(q, I)$$

for each I in Σ. Since $\lambda[\delta(p, I), N] = \lambda[\delta(q, I), N]$ for each tape N of length $2n - 2$, it will result that $p \overset{2n-1}{\equiv} q$. From Theorem 1.2, it will follow that $p \equiv q$, whence $p \sim q$.

To see that $p = p_n$ and $q = q_n$, we first show that $\delta(p, I) = p_1$ and $\delta(q, I) = q_1$ for each I in Σ. To this end, let I be in Σ. Suppose that $\delta(p, I) \neq p_1$. By (ii), $\delta(p, I) = p_i$ for some i, $1 < i \leq n$. Let $\delta(q, I) = q_j$, where $1 \leq j \leq n$. Two cases arise.

(1) $i = j$. Since $p \overset{2n-1}{\sim} q$ is false via the tape J, $p_i \overset{2n-1-i}{\sim} q_i$ is also false. Since $p \overset{2n-2}{\sim} q$, then $p_i = \delta(p, I) \overset{2n-3}{\sim} \delta(q, I) = q_i$. Since $p_i \overset{2n-3}{\sim} q_i$ and $i + 1 \geq 3$, it follows that $p_i \overset{2n-1-i}{\sim} q_i$. This is a contradiction.

(2) $i \neq j$. Since $p \overset{2n-2}{\sim} q$, then $p_i \overset{2n-1-i}{\equiv} q_i$ and $p_i = \delta(p, I) \overset{2n-2}{\equiv} \delta(q, I) = q_j$. Thus $p_i \overset{n-1}{\equiv} q_i$ and $p_i \overset{n-1}{\equiv} q_j$. Then $q_i \overset{n-1}{\equiv} q_j$. Therefore $q_i \equiv q_j$. As T is a distinguished machine, $q_i = q_j$. Since $q_1, \ldots, q_n$ are the n states in T, $i = j$. This is a contradiction.

Thus $\delta(p, I) = p_1$. Similarly $\delta(q, I) = q_1$ for each I in Σ.

By (ii), $p = p_i$ for some i, $1 \leq i \leq n$. Then $p_1 = p_{i+1}$. If $i < n$, then $\{p_1, \ldots, p_n\}$ is not a set of n states, contradicting (ii). Therefore $i = n$. Thus $p = p_n$. Similarly $q = q_n$. Thus (b) is proved.

To prove (c), it is sufficient to assume that $m \leq n$. The case $m = 1$ is left to the reader. Assume $m > 1$. Suppose that $m = n$. Let

$$A = (K_A, \{I^1\}, \delta_A, p_1, \{p_n\}) \quad \text{and} \quad B = (K_B, \{I^1\}, \delta_B, q_1, \{q_n\}),$$

where

$$K_A = \{p_i | 1 \leq i \leq n\}, \quad K_B = \{q_i | 1 \leq i \leq n\},$$

$$\delta_A(p_i, I^1) = p_{i+1} \quad \text{for } i < n,$$

$$\delta_A(p_n, I^1) = p_1,$$

$$\delta_B(q_i, I^1) = q_{i+1} \quad \text{for } i < n,$$

and

$$\delta_B(q_n, I^1) = q_2.$$

It is readily seen that $p_1 \overset{2n-3}{\sim} q_1$, but $p_1 \overset{2n-2}{\sim} q_1$ is false. Suppose that $m < n$. Let

$$A = (K_A, \{I^1, I^2\}, \delta_A, p_1, \{p_1\})$$

and

$$B = (K_B, \{I^1, I^2\}, \delta_B, q_1, F_B),$$

where

$$K_A = \{p_i | 1 \leq i \leq m\},$$

$$K_B = \{q_i | 1 \leq i \leq n\},$$

$$F_B = \left\{ q_{km+1} | 1 \leq k \leq \frac{n-1}{m} \right\},$$

$$\delta_A(p_i, I^1) = p_{i+1} \quad \text{for } i < m,$$

$$\delta_A(p_m, I^1) = p_1,$$

$$\delta_A(p_i, I^2) = p_2 \quad \text{for all } i,$$

$$\delta_B(q_i, I^1) = q_{i+1} \quad \text{for } i < n,$$

$$\delta_B(q_n, I^1) = q_{n-m+1},$$

$$\delta_B(q_i, I^2) = q_2 \quad \text{for all } i < n,$$

and

$$\delta_B(q_n, I^2) = q_1.$$

It is readily seen that $p_1 \overset{m+n-2}{\sim} q_1$, but $p_1 \overset{m+n-1}{\sim} q_1$ is false. In fact, if $J = (I^1)^{n-1} I^2 (I^1)^{m-1}$, then $\delta_A(p_1, J)$ is in F_A, but $\delta_B(q_1, J)$ is not in F_B.

Corollary. Let $A = (K_A, \Sigma, \delta_A, p_1, F_A)$ and $B = (K_B, \Sigma, \delta_B, q_1, F_B)$ be non ϵ-automata with m and n states, respectively. If $p_1 \overset{m+n-1}{\sim} q_1$, then $T(A) = T(B)$. If $m = n > 1$ and $p_1 \overset{m+n-2}{\sim} q_1$, then $T(A) = T(B)$. If $m \neq n$, then $m + n - 1$ is the smallest possible number in the general case. If $m = n > 1$, then $m + n - 2$ is the smallest possible number in the general case.

EXERCISE 1. Determine the non ϵ-automata A and B in (c) of Theorem 4.6 when (i) $m = 4$ and $n = 4$, (ii) $m = 3$ and $n = 7$.

Prove each of the following.

EXERCISE 2. Lemma 4.2.

EXERCISE 3. $T(A)$ is nonempty if and only if there exists a tape in $T(A)$ of length $\leq \#(K_A)$.

EXERCISE 4. $T(A)$ is infinite if and only if it contains a tape in $T(A)$ of length r, where $n \leq r \leq 2n$ and $n = \#(K_A)$.

4.5 Other recognition devices. The basic recognition device studied so far is the automaton. An automaton recognizes whether or not to accept a tape by means of a set of "final" states. In this section we consider various finite-state devices which recognize tapes by other means. Among these are (i) last input and next to last state, (ii) last state and last output, and (iii) last outputs. We shall see that the discriminatory power of the resulting devices is exactly the same as that of automata, namely, the family of regular sets. The family of regular sets thus is a ubiquitous family with respect to finite-state recognition devices.

In this section only, an automaton is called a 1-automaton. In order to simplify the definitions to be introduced, it is also convenient in this section to disallow ϵ as a tape. No real generality is lost, since the concepts to be introduced could be altered slightly to allow ϵ.

Notation. Denote by Z_1 the family of Σ-regular sets.

Notation. If δ is a mapping of $K \times \Sigma$ onto K, then $\delta(q, I_1 \ldots I_{k-1}) = q$ if $k = 1$.

Definition 4.9. A *2-automaton* is a 5-tuple $A = (K, \Sigma, \delta, s_0, F)$, where δ is a function of $K \times \Sigma$ into K, s_0 is an element of K, and F is a set of ordered pairs (q, I) of elements q in K and I in Σ.

Notation. For each 2-automaton $A = (K, \Sigma, \delta, s_0, F)$, denote by $T(A)$ the set of those tapes $I_1 \ldots I_k$ having the property that

$$\big(\delta(s_0, I_1 \ldots I_{k-1}), I_k\big)$$

is in F. Denote by Z_2 the family of $T(A)$ for all 2-automata A.

A 2-automaton is a recognition device which discriminates tapes by means of last inputs and next to last states.

Lemma 4.3. $Z_2 = Z_1$.

Proof. Let $A = (K, \Sigma, \delta, s_0, F)$ be a 1-automaton. Consider the 2-automaton $B = (K, \Sigma, \delta, s_0, H)$, where $H = \{(q, I) | I$ in Σ, $\delta(q, I)$ is in $F\}$. Clearly $T(A) = T(B)$. Thus $Z_1 \subseteq Z_2$.

Let $A = (K, \Sigma, \delta, s_0, F)$ be a 2-automaton and $U = T(A)$. Consider the relation R defined as follows. For two tapes $I = I_1 \ldots I_k$ and $J = J_1 \ldots J_r$, $I R J$ if and only if $I_k = J_r$ and $\delta(s_0, I_1 \ldots I_{k-1}) = \delta(s_0, J_1 \ldots J_{r-1})$. Clearly R is an equivalence relation, and the number of equivalence classes generated by R is at most $\#(K)\#(\Sigma)$. Let $\sim$ be the right invariant equivalence relation defined in (iii) of Theorem 4.4. Suppose that $I R J$ for the tapes I and J. Then for some I_1 in Σ, $I = M_1 I_1$, $J = M_2 I_1$, and $\delta(s_0, M_1) = \delta(s_0, M_2)$. Let W be any tape. Then $W = M_3 I_3$ for some I_3 in Σ. Thus $IW = I M_3 I_3$ and $JW = J M_3 I_3$. Also

$$
\begin{aligned}
\delta(s_0, IM_3) &= \delta(s_0, M_1 I_1 M_3) \\
&= \delta[\delta(s_0, M_1), I_1 M_3] \\
&= \delta[\delta(s_0, M_2), I_1 M_3] \\
&= \delta(s_0, M_2 I_1 M_3) = \delta(s_0, JM_3).
\end{aligned}
$$

Thus IW is in U if and only if JW is in U. In other words, for any tapes I and J, $I \sim J$ if $I R J$. Then the number of equivalence classes generated by $\sim$ is at most $\#(K)\#(\Sigma)$ and therefore finite. By Theorem 4.4, U is regular. Thus $Z_2 \subseteq Z_1$. Therefore $Z_2 = Z_1$.

For the remainder of this section, Δ is the set $\{0, 1, \ldots, m - 1\}$, m being a fixed integer ≥ 2.

Definition 4.10. A *3-automaton* is a 7-tuple $A = (K, \Sigma, \Delta, \delta, \lambda, s_0, F)$ which satisfies the following: δ is a function from $K \times \Sigma$ into K, λ is a function from $K \times \Sigma$ into Δ, s_0 is in K, and F is a set of ordered pairs (q, E) of elements q in K and E in Δ.

Notation. Let $A = (K, \Sigma, \Delta, \delta, \lambda, s_0, F)$ be a 3-automaton. Denote by $T(A)$ the set of those tapes $I_1 \ldots I_k$ having the property that

$$\big(\delta(p, I_k), \lambda(p, I_k)\big)$$

is in F, where $p = \delta(s_0, I_1 \ldots I_{k-1})$. Let Z_3 be the family of $T(A)$ for all 3-automata A.

A 3-automaton is a recognition device, with an output function, which distinguishes tapes by means of last states and last outputs.

Lemma 4.4. $Z_3 = Z_1$.

Proof. Let $A = (K, \Sigma, \delta, s_0, F)$ be any 1-automaton. Consider the 3-automaton $B = (K, \Sigma, \Delta, \delta, \lambda, s_0, H)$, where
  (i) $\lambda(q, I) = 1$ if $\delta(q, I)$ is in F,
  (ii) $\lambda(q, I) = 0$ if $\delta(q, I)$ is not in F, and
  (iii) $H = \{(p, 1)|p$ in $F\}$.
Then $T(B) = T(A)$. Thus $Z_2 = Z_1 \subseteq Z_3$.
Let $A = (K, \Sigma, \Delta, \delta, \lambda, s_0, F)$ be any 3-automaton. By a method similar to that used in Lemma 4.3, it is easily seen that $T(A)$ is a regular set. Thus $Z_3 \subseteq Z_2$. Therefore $Z_3 = Z_2 = Z_1$.

Definition 4.11. A *4-automaton* is a 3-automaton

$$A = (K, \Sigma, \Delta, \delta, \lambda, s_0, F)$$

where, for a fixed element E in Δ, $F = \{(q, E)|q$ in $K\}$.

If A is a 4-automaton, then A is a 3-automaton. Thus $T(A)$ is defined. The set $T(A)$ consists of those tapes which, when applied to the 4-automaton initially at state s_0, yield a fixed final output E.

Notation. Let Z_4 be the family of $T(A)$ for all 4-automata A.

Lemma 4.5. $Z_4 = Z_1$.

Proof. By definition, Z_4 is a subset of Z_3. Let $A = (K, \Sigma, \Delta, \delta, \lambda, s_0, F)$ be a 3-automaton. Let $H = \{(q, 1)|q$ in $K\}$. For q in K and I in Σ, define $\lambda_B(q, I) = 1$ if $(\delta(q, I), \lambda(q, I))$ is in F and $\lambda_B(q, I) = 0$ otherwise. Consider the 4-automaton $B = (K, \Sigma, \Delta, \delta, \lambda_B, s_0, H)$. The tape $I_1 \ldots I_k$ being in $T(A)$ is equivalent to $(\delta(q, I_k), \lambda(q, I_k))$ being in F, where $q = \delta(s_0, I_1 \ldots I_{k-1})$. This is equivalent to $(\delta(q, I_k), \lambda_B(q, I_k))$ being in H, which, in turn, is equivalent to $I_1 \ldots I_k$ being in $T(B)$. Then $Z_3 \subseteq Z_4$. Thus $Z_4 = Z_3 = Z_1$.
The fifth and last type of automaton to be described is the following.

Definition 4.12. A *5-automaton* is a 7-tuple $A = (K, \Sigma, \Delta, \delta, \lambda, s_0, F)$ which satisfies the following: δ is a function from $K \times \Sigma$ into K, λ is a function from $K \times \Sigma$ into Δ, s_0 is an element of K, and F is a finite set of nonempty finite sequences $E^1 \ldots E^r$ of elements from Δ (r depends on the sequence in F and is not necessarily fixed).

Notation. Let $A = (K, \Sigma, \Delta, \delta, \lambda, s_0, F)$ be a 5-automaton. Denote by $T(A)$ the set of those tapes $I_1 \ldots I_k$ having the property that the output sequence $\lambda(s_0, I_1 \ldots I_k)$ terminates in a sequence which is in F. Let Z_5 be the family of $T(A)$ for all 5-automata A.

A 5-automaton is thus a device which recognizes a tape by the terminal end of the output sequence.

Lemma 4.6. $Z_5 = Z_1$.

Proof. Clearly $Z_1 = Z_4 \subseteq Z_5$. To show the reverse inclusion, let $A = (K, \Sigma, \Delta, \delta, \lambda, s_0, F)$ be a 5-automaton. Let $E^1 \ldots E^r$ be any element of F. We shall show that the set U of those tapes $I_1 \ldots I_k$ for which the sequence of outputs $\lambda(s_0, I_1 \ldots I_k)$ terminates in $E^1 \ldots E^r$ is regular. Since $E^1 \ldots E^r$ is any element of F, it will follow that there exists a finite family $\{U_1, \ldots, U_t\}$ of regular sets such that $T(A) = \cup_{i=1}^t U_i$. Hence it will follow that $T(A)$ is a regular set, that is, $Z_5 \subseteq Z_1$, whence $Z_5 = Z_1$.

To show that U is regular, let the relation R be defined as follows: $I = I_1 \ldots I_k$ and $J = J_1 \ldots J_m$, $I \; R \; J$ if and only if $k \geq r$, $m \geq r$, $\delta(s_0, I) = \delta(s_0, J)$, and $\lambda(p, I_{k-r+1} \ldots I_k) = \lambda(q, J_{m-r+1} \ldots J_m)$, where $p = \delta(s_0, I_1 \ldots I_{k-r})$ and $q = \delta(s_0, J_1 \ldots J_{m-r})$. Clearly R is an equivalence relation. The number of equivalence classes generated by R is at most $\#(K)\#(\Sigma)^r + L$, where L is the number of tapes of length less than r. Let $\sim$ be the right invariant equivalence relation defined in (iii) of Theorem 4.4. As in Lemma 4.3 it is readily seen that $\sim$ is of finite index, so that U is regular.

Remark. If the definition of a 5-automaton is extended to letting F be an infinite set of tapes, then Lemma 4.6 is no longer true. Thus let $K = \{s_0\}$, $\Sigma = \{a, b\}$, $\delta(s_0, a) = \delta(s_0, b) = s_0$, $\lambda(s_0, a) = E^0$, and $\lambda(s_0, b) = E^1$. Let F be the infinite set

$$F = \{(E^0)^n (E^1)^n | n \geq 1\}.$$

Consider $T(A)$, where $A = (K, \Sigma, \{E^0, E^1\}, \delta, \lambda, s_0, F)$. Then

$$T(A) = \{(a)^n (b)^n | n \geq 1\} \cup \{X(a)^n (b)^n | n \geq 1; \text{all tapes } X\}.$$

By methods similar to those used in example 5, Section 4.3, it is seen that $T(A)$ is not regular.

For $1 \leq x \leq 5$, each x-automaton is a *complete* automaton in the sense that δ (and λ when pertinent) is a function defined on all of $K \times \Sigma$. We now consider *incomplete* x-automata, where by incomplete is meant that δ (or λ when pertinent) is defined on a *subset* of $K \times \Sigma$. Thus, by definition, a complete automaton is also an incomplete automaton.

Definition 4.13. An *incomplete 1-automaton* is a 5-tuple

$$A = (K, \Sigma, \delta, s_0, F),$$

where δ maps a subset of $K \times \Sigma$ into K, s_0 is an element of K, and F is a subset of K.

Notation. For each incomplete 1-automaton A, denote by $T(A)$ the set of those tapes J having the property that $\delta(s_0, J)$ exists and is in F. Denote by $\overline{Z}_1$ the family of $T(A)$ for all incomplete 1-automata A.

In view of the fact that an incomplete 1-automaton is a nondeterministic automaton, to each incomplete 1-automaton A there is a complete 1-automaton B such that $T(A) = T(B)$. Thus

Lemma 4.7. $\overline{Z}_1 = Z_1$.

The definition of an incomplete 2-automaton A, $T(A)$, and $\overline{Z}_2$ is analogous to the definition of an incomplete 1-automaton A, $T(A)$, and $\overline{Z}_1$. In view of Lemma 4.7 and the method of proof of Lemma 4.3, we arrive at

Lemma 4.8. $\overline{Z}_2 = Z_1$.

Incomplete 3-automata and incomplete 4-automata are now defined by allowing δ and λ to be functions from subsets of $K \times \Sigma$ into K and Δ, respectively. For these incomplete automata $A = (K, \Sigma, \Delta, \delta, \lambda, s_0, F)$, $T(A)$ is defined as the set of those tapes $I_1 \ldots I_k$ satisfying the following properties: (i) $\delta(s_0, I_1 \ldots I_k)$ exists, (ii) $\lambda(s_0, I_1 \ldots I_k)$ exists, and (iii) $\big(\delta(q, I_k), \lambda(q, I_k)\big)$ is in F, where $q = \delta(s_0, I_1 \ldots I_{k-1})$. The resulting families of sets of $T(A)$ are denoted by $\overline{Z}_3$ and $\overline{Z}_4$, respectively. By a slight modification of Lemmas 4.4 and 4.5, and by using Lemmas 4.7 and 4.8, we can show that $\overline{Z}_3 = \overline{Z}_4 = Z_1$. Similar comments hold for incomplete 5-automata, with the end result that $\overline{Z}_5 = Z_1$.
Summarizing, we have

Theorem 4.7. $Z_x = \overline{Z}_y$ for $1 \leq x, y \leq 5$.

EXERCISES. Prove each of the following.

1. Show that $\overline{Z}_1 = Z_1$ without appealing to nondeterministic automata.
2. Show, without using Theorem 4.4, that (i) $Z_1 = Z_2$, (ii) $Z_1 = Z_3$, and (iii) $Z_1 = Z_5$.
3. Show that $\overline{Z}_2 = \overline{Z}_3 = \overline{Z}_4 = \overline{Z}_5 = Z_1$.
4. Let $A = (K, \Sigma, \Delta, \delta, \lambda, s_0, F)$, where F is a Δ-regular set. Then the set of those tapes J for which $\lambda(s_0, J)$ is in F is Σ-regular.
5. Let $A = (K, \Sigma, \Delta, \delta, \lambda, s_0, F)$, where F is a Δ-regular set. Then the set of those tapes J for which $\lambda(s_0, J)$ ends in a sequence in F is Σ-regular. This generalizes Lemma 4.6. [*Hint:* Use exercise 4.]
6. How would you generalize the x-automata, $2 \leq x \leq 5$, so as to distinguish between tapes in a family of disjoint sets, much as the general recognition device mentioned in Section 4.1 generalizes the automaton?

4.6 Two-way automata. In all the devices studied so far the tapes move unilaterally, namely, from the right to the left.* The next input is always located immediately to the right of the current one. We now consider a device in which the tape moves bilaterally, that is, both to the left and to the right. This means that an input in the tape may be used more than once. The device keeps on functioning until it goes off the tape at either the left or the right end. The device is to accept a tape if the device goes off the tape at the right end, and simultaneously, the terminal state is an element of a specified set.

Definition 4.14. Let $L = \{-1, 0, 1\}$. A *two-way automaton* is a 5-tuple $A = (K, \Sigma, \delta, s_0, F)$, where δ is a function from $K \times \Sigma$ into $L \times K$, s_0 is an element of K, and F is a subset of K.

It is assumed that $\delta(q, \epsilon) = (1, q)$ for each state q.

Notation. For each two-way automaton A, denote by $T(A)$ the set of those tapes $I_1 \ldots I_k$ for which there exists an integer $m > 0$, a sequence of integers $b_1, \ldots, b_{m+1}$, and a sequence $s_0 = q_1, \ldots, q_{m+1}$ of elements of K with the following properties:
  (i) $b_1 = 1$.
  (ii) $1 \le b_i \le k$ for $i = 1, \ldots, m$.
  (iii) $b_{m+1} = k + 1$ and q_{m+1} is in F.
  (iv) $(b_{i+1} - b_i, q_{i+1}) = \delta(q_i, I_{b_i})$ for $i = 1, \ldots, m$.
In particular, the empty tape ϵ is in $T(A)$ if and only if s_0 is in K.

The sequence $b_1, \ldots, b_{m+1}$ is to be interpreted as the sequence of positions of the tape as it enters the device. The integer $b_{i+1} - b_i$ indicates the change in position from time i to time $i + 1$. Conditions (ii) and (iii) of the notation state that the machine is not to go off the tape until the $(m + 1)$th time.

EXAMPLE 1. Let $A = (K, \Sigma, \delta, s_0, F)$, where $s_0 = p_1$, $F = \{p_3\}$, and δ is given in Fig. 4.9. Consider the tape $X = I^1 I^2 I^2$. Then $I_1 = I^1$, $I_2 = I^2$, and $I_3 = I^2$. The behavior of the two-way automaton to the tape is indicated pictorially by

I^1	I^2	I^2	I^2	
$(1, p_1)$	$(2, p_2)$	$(2, p_3)$	$(3, p_3)$	$(4, p_3)$
$b_1 = 1$	$b_2 = 2$	$b_3 = 2$	$b_4 = 3$	$b_5 = 4$

Since p_3 is in F and the tape goes off the right end, X is in $T(A)$. Similarly it is seen that the tape $I^1 I^1 I^1 I^2 I^2$ is not in $T(A)$. In fact, for each tape J, $I^1 I^1 J$ is not in $T(A)$.

As far as the problem of recognition is concerned, the basic fact about two-way automata is that they are no more potent than one-way automata.

----

* The position at which each input is inserted into the device is assumed fixed.

	I^1		I^2	
p_1	1	p_2	-1	p_2
p_2	-1	p_1	0	p_3
p_3	-1	p_2	1	p_3

FIGURE 4.9

	I^1		I^2	
p_1	1	p_2	1	p_3
p_2	1	p_3	1	p_4
p_3	-1	p_3	-1	p_3
p_4	1	p_2	1	p_1

FIGURE 4.10

Theorem 4.8. For each two-way automaton A, $T(A)$ is a regular set.

Proof. Let $A = (K, \Sigma, \delta, s_0, F)$ be a two-way automaton. To show that $T(A)$ is regular, consider the relation $\sim$ defined in (iii) of Theorem 4.4. That is, for two tapes X_1 and X_2, write $X_1 \sim X_2$ if $X_1 X$ is in $T(A)$ if and only if $X_2 X$ is in $T(A)$ for each tape X. We shall prove that the right invariant relation $\sim$ is of finite index. By Theorem 4.4 it will follow that $T(A)$ is regular.

Let p_1 be a symbol which is not in K. For each tape $X = I_1 \ldots I_k$, define a function τ_X of $\{p_1\} \cup K$ into $\{p_1\} \cup K$ as follows. For each state q in K, let $\tau_X(q) = q'$ if A, started at q on the *rightmost* symbol of X, ultimately goes off the tape from the right, going into the state q'; and let $\tau_X(q) = p_1$ otherwise. Let $\tau_X(p_1) = q'$ if A, started at s_0 on the *leftmost* symbol of X, ultimately goes off the tape from the right, going into the state q'; and let $\tau_X(p_1) = p_1$ otherwise. It is readily verified that $X_1 \sim X_2$ if $\tau_{X_1} = \tau_{X_2}$ (see exercise 2). Thus the number of equivalence classes generated by $\sim$ is at most the number of different functions τ_X. Since $\#(\{p_1\} \cup K) = \#(K) + 1$, there are at most $[\#(K) + 1]^{\#(K)+1}$ different functions τ_X. Therefore $\sim$ is of finite index.

EXERCISE 1. Let $A = (K, \Sigma, \delta, p_1, \{p_1\})$, where δ is given in Fig. 4.10. (a) Find two tapes in $T(A)$. (b) Find two tapes not in $T(A)$.

EXERCISE 2. Verify in the proof of Theorem 4.8 that $X_1 \sim X_2$ if $\tau_{X_1} = \tau_{X_2}$.

EXERCISE 3. Let $A = (K, \Sigma, \delta, s_0, F)$ be a two-way automaton. Let $T_1(A)$ be the set of those tapes $I_1 \ldots I_k$ for which there exists an integer $m > 0$, a sequence of integers $b_1, \ldots, b_{m+1}$, and a sequence $s_0 = q_1, \ldots, q_{m+1}$ of elements of K with the following properties:

(i) $b_1 = 1$.
(ii) $1 \leq b_i \leq k$ for $i = 1, \ldots, m$.
(iii) $b_{m+1} = 0$ or $k + 1$.
(iv) q_{m+1} is in F.
(v) $(b_{i+1} - b_i, q_{i+1}) = \delta(q_i, I_{b_i})$ for $i = 1, \ldots, m$.

Show that $T_1(A)$ is regular. [$T_1(A)$ is the set of those tapes for which the device, starting at s_0, goes off the tape at either the left or the right, and terminates in a state of F.]

4.7 Two-tape automata. We now consider a recognition device with two tapes. A two-tape automaton is an abstraction of a physical device with two "scanning heads" which "reads" a pair (X_1, X_2) of tapes. The functioning of the device A is as follows. One tape is fed into the machine for a while, then the other tape, then the first, etc., until one of the tapes is exhausted. A then stops and the pair (X_1, X_2) is accepted if and only if A is in a designated final state.

Definition 4.15. A *two-tape* automaton is a 7-tuple

$$A = (K, \Sigma, \delta, s_0, F, C_1, C_2),$$

where $(K, \Sigma, \delta, s_0, F)$ is an automaton, $C_1 \cap C_2 = \emptyset$, and $C_1 \cup C_2 = K$.

The interpretation is that states in C_1 concern the first tape and states in C_2 the second.

Notation. Let A be a two-tape automaton and let $s_0, \ldots, s_t$ be a sequence of states. Then there is a unique pair of associated sequences of integers $(u_0, \ldots, u_t; v_0, \ldots, v_t)$ such that
   (i) u_i is either 1 or 2 according as s_i is in C_1 or C_2.
   (ii) v_i is the number of indices $j \leq i$ such that s_j is in C_{u_i}.

The integers u_i and v_i perform the following function. u_i keeps track of which set, C_1 or C_2, the current state s_i belongs to. v_i keeps track of the position of the input on the tape being read.

Definition 4.16. Let $A = (K, \Sigma, \delta, s_0, F, C_1, C_2)$ be a two-tape automaton. The pair $(X_1, X_2) = (I_{11} \ldots I_{1m}, I_{21} \ldots I_{2n})$ of tapes is said to be *accepted* by A if there is a (unique) sequence of states $s_0, \ldots, s_t$ and pair of associated sequences of integers $(u_0, \ldots, u_t; v_0, \ldots, v_t)$ satisfying the following:
   (i) $s_i = \delta(s_{i-1}, I_{u_{i-1}v_{i-1}})$ for $i = 1, \ldots, t$.
   (ii) s_t is in F.
   (iii) If $u_t = 1$, then $v_t = m + 1$, and if $u_t = 2$, then $v_t = n + 1$.*
The set of all accepted pairs of tapes (X_1, X_2) is denoted by $T_2(A)$.

---

* In the literature [R1], condition (iii) has been replaced by the following: (iv) If $u_t = 1$, then $v_t = m$, and if $u_t = 2$, then $v_t = n$. When (iv) is used instead of (iii), I_{1m} and I_{2n} are special end-of-tape markers not in Σ which cause no next states to occur. There are slight differences in the effects of (iii) and (iv).

	I^1	I^2
p_1	p_2	p_4
p_2	p_2	p_3
p_3	p_1	p_4
p_4	p_2	p_3

FIGURE 4.11

EXAMPLE 1. Let $A = (K, \Sigma, \delta, p_1, \{p_3, p_4\}, \{p_1, p_2\}, \{p_3, p_4\})$, where δ is given in Fig. 4.11. Consider the pair of tapes

$$(I^1I^1I^2I^2, I^2I^1) = (I_{11}I_{12}I_{13}I_{14}, I_{21}I_{22}).$$

Applying the pair of tapes, we get

$$
\begin{array}{cccccc}
I^1 & I^1 & I^2 & I^2 & I^1 & I^2 \\
I_{11} & I_{12} & I_{13} & I_{21} & I_{22} & I_{14} \\
p_1 & p_2 & p_2 & p_3 & p_4 & p_2 & p_3
\end{array}
$$

Since p_3 is in F, the pair of tapes is accepted.

EXERCISE 1. Is $(I^2I^1I^1, I^2I^2I^1I^2)$ accepted by the two-tape automaton in example 1?

In contrast with regular sets, very little is known about the structure of sets $T_2(A)$. We shall see (Theorem 4.10) that the family of sets definable by two-tape automata (i) is closed under complementation, (ii) is not closed under intersection and union.

Unsolved problem. Characterize the family of sets definable by two-tape automata.

In order to prove Theorem 4.10 we need a preliminary result relating sets definable by two-tape automata to regular sets. This result is also of interest in its own right.

Theorem 4.9. Let $A = (K, \Sigma, \delta, s_0, F, C_1, C_2)$ be a two-tape automaton. The set of all tapes X_1 for which there exists some tape X_2 such that (X_1, X_2) is in $T_2(A)$ is a regular set.

Proof. Let D be the set of tapes X_1 for which there exists some tape X_2 such that (X_1, X_2) is in $T_2(A)$. We shall construct a nondeterministic automaton B for which $D = T(B)$.

For states q_1 in C_1 and q_2 in C_2, call a tape $X = I_1 \ldots I_k$ a (q_2, q_1) *transition* tape if it satisfies the following condition: For each i let $p_i = \delta(q_2, I_1 \ldots I_i)$; then there exists an integer u such that $p_u = q_1$ and p_j is in C_2 for $j < u$. For every such pair (q_2, q_1) for which there exists a transition tape, let $X(q_2, q_1)$ denote one of smallest length.

Call a state q_2 in C_2 a *finalizing* state if there exists a tape $X(q_2) = I_1 \ldots I_k$ satisfying the following condition: For each i let $p_i = \delta(q_2, I_1 \ldots I_i)$; then each p_i is in C_2 and p_k is in $F \cap C_2$.

Let B be the nondeterministic automaton $(K_B, \Sigma, \delta_B, S_0, G)$ defined as follows. Let q_0 be an abstract symbol not in K_A and let $K_B = C_1 \cup \{q_0\}$. Let δ_B be the function defined as follows for each I in Σ and q in C_1.

  (i) $\delta_B(q_0, I) = \{q_0\}$.
  (ii) $\delta_B(q, I) = \{\delta_A(q, I)\}$ if $\delta_A(q, I)$ is in C_1.
  (iii) $\delta_B(q, I) = \{q_0\}$ if $\delta_A(q, I)$ is a finalizing state in C_2.
  (iv) $\delta_B(q, I) = \delta_*(q, I)$ if $\delta_A(q, I)$ is in C_2 and is not a finalizing state. Here $\delta_*(q, I)$ is the set of those states q_1 for which there exists a transition tape $X(\delta_A(q, I), q_1)$.

The set S_0 of start states of B is $\{s_0\}$ if s_0 is in C_1, and is the set of those q_1 for which there exists a tape $X(s_0, q_1)$ if s_0 is in C_2. Finally, let $G = (C_1 \cap F) \cup \{q_0\}$.

It is left as an exercise to show that $T(B) = D$.

We now consider the family of all sets definable by two-tape automata.

Theorem 4.10. The family of all sets definable by two-tape automata is (i) closed under complementation, and (ii) not closed under set intersection or set union.

Proof. (i) Suppose we are given $T_2(A)$, where

$$A = (K, \Sigma, \delta, s_0, F, C_1, C_2).$$

Then $\theta \times \theta - T_2(A) = T_2(B)$, where $B = (K, \Sigma, \delta, s_0, K - F, C_1, C_2)$.

(ii) Let $A = (K_A, \Sigma, \delta_A, q_1, \{q_1\}, \{q_1, q_4\}, \{q_2, q_3\})$, where δ_A is in Fig. 4.12. Then

$$T_2(A) = \{(J, JX)| \text{all tapes } J \text{ and } X\}.$$

Let $B = (K_B, \Sigma, \delta_B, p_1, \{p_4\}, \{p_1, p_2, p_4, p_6\}, \{p_3, p_5\})$, where δ_B is in Fig. 4.13. Then

$$T_2(B) = \{((a)^i(b)^n, (a)^n X)| i \geq 1, n \geq 1, \text{all tapes } X\}.$$

Suppose that

$$T_2(C) = T_2(A) \cap T_2(B)$$
$$= \{((a)^n(b)^n, (a)^n(b)^n Y)| n \geq 1, \text{all tapes } Y\}$$

	a	b
q_1	q_2	q_3
q_2	q_1	q_4
q_3	q_4	q_1
q_4	q_4	q_4

FIGURE 4.12

	a	b
p_1	p_2	p_5
p_2	p_2	p_3
p_3	p_4	p_5
p_4	p_5	p_3
p_5	p_5	p_5

FIGURE 4.13

for some two-tape automaton C. By Theorem 4.9, the set $\{(a)^n(b)^n | n \geq 1\}$ is regular. But, as shown in example 5 of Section 3, this set is not regular. Therefore $T_2(A) \cap T_2(B)$ is not the set of pairs of tapes accepted by a two-tape automaton. Thus the family is not closed under intersection. Since closure under complementation and union implies closure under intersection, the family is not closed under union.

EXERCISE 2. In the proof of Theorem 4.9, show that $T(B) = D$.

EXERCISE 3. If A is a two-tape automaton and (I, J) is in $T_2(A)$, show that either $\{(IX, J) | \text{all } X\} \subseteq T_2(A)$ or $\{(I, JX) | \text{all } X\} \subseteq T_2(A)$. Thus infer that $T_2(A)$ is either empty or infinite.

EXERCISE 4. For each tape I, prove that the set $\{J | (I, J) \text{ in } T_2(A)\}$ is regular.

Unsolved Problem. Find a suitable definition for devices A which "accept" sets $T_n(A)$ consisting of n-tuples of tapes. Characterize the family Y_n of all sets $T_n(A)$ and find relations between Y_n and Y_{n-1}.

4.8 History. Regular sets and automata first appeared in [K2] in a different formulation. The proof of (b) of Theorem 4.2 given here is that found in [M1]. Theorem 4.5 is new. Theorem 4.6 is an unpublished result from the work of T. N. Hibbard. The x-automata, $x \geq 2$, are found in [G9]. The remaining recognition devices and text material, with the exception of the proof of Theorem 4.8, are drawn from [R1]. The proof of Theorem 4.8 is from [S1].

BIBLIOGRAPHY

The following references are cited in the text.

[A1] Aufenkamp, D. D., "Analysis of Sequential Machines II," *IRE Transactions on Electronic Computers*, **EC7,** 299–306 (1958).

[C1] Caldwell, S., *Switching Circuits and Logical Design*. New York: John Wiley and Sons, 1959.

[D1] Davis, M., *Computability and Unsolvability*. New York: McGraw-Hill, 1958.

[G1] Gill, A., "A Note on Moore's Distinguishability Theorem," *IRE Transactions on Electronic Computers*, **EC10,** 290–291 (1961).

[G2] Ginsburg, S., "On the Length of the Smallest Uniform Experiment Which Distinguishes the Terminal States of a Machine," *Journal of the Association for Computing Machinery*, **5,** 266–280 (1958).

[G3] Ginsburg, S., "On the Reduction of Superfluous States in a Sequential Machine," *Journal of the Association for Computing Machinery*, **6,** 259–282 (1959).

[G4] Ginsburg, S., "Synthesis of Minimal-State Machines," *IRE Transactions on Electronic Computers*, **EC8,** 441–449 (1959).

[G5] Ginsburg, S., "A Technique for the Reduction of a Given Machine to a Minimal-State Machine," *IRE Transactions on Electronic Computers*, **EC8,** 346–355 (1959).

[G6] Ginsburg, S., "Some Remarks on Abstract Machines," *Transactions of the American Mathematical Society*, **96,** 400–444 (1960).

[G7] Ginsburg, S., "Examples of Abstract Machines," to appear in the *IRE Transactions on Electronic Computers*, April 1962.

[G8] Ginsburg, S., and E. H. Spanier, "Distinguishability of a Semi-Group by a Machine," *Proceedings of the American Mathematical Society*, **12,** 661–668 (1961).

[G9] Ginsburg, S., "Sets of Tapes Accepted by Different Types of Automata," *Journal of the Association for Computing Machinery*, **8,** 81–86 (1961).

[H1] Hibbard, T. N., "Least Upper Bounds on Minimal Terminal State Experiments for Two Classes of Sequential Machines," *Journal of the Association for Computing Machinery*, **8,** 601–612 (1961).

[H2] Huffman, D. A., "The Synthesis of Sequential Switching Circuits," *Journal of the Franklin Institute*, **257,** 161–190, 275–303 (1954).

[K1] Karatsuba, A. A., "Solution of a Problem from the Theory of Finite Automata," (in Russian) English translation by Morris Friedman, Inc.

[K2] Kleene, S. C., "Representation of Events in Nerve Nets and Finite Automata," *Automata Studies*, pp. 3–41, Princeton University Press, 1956.

[M1] McNaughton, R. F., and H. Yamada, "Regular Expressions and State Graphs for Automata," *IRE Transactions on Electronic Computers*, **EC9,** 39–47 (1960).

[M2] Mealy, G. H., "A Method for Synthesizing Sequential Circuits," *Bell System Technical Journal*, **34,** 1045–1079 (1955).

[M3] MOORE, E. F., "Gedanken-Experiments on Sequential Machines," *Automata Studies*, pp. 129–153, Princeton University Press, 1956.

[P1] PAULL, M. C., and S. H. UNGER, "Minimizing the Number of States in Incompletely Specified Sequential Switching Functions," *IRE Transactions on Electronic Computers*, **EC8**, 356–367 (1959).

[R1] RABIN, M. O., and D. SCOTT, "Finite Automata and Their Decision Problems," *IBM Journal of Research and Development*, **3**, 114–125 (1959).

[S1] SHEPHERDSON, J. C., "The Reduction of Two-Way Automata to One-Way Automata," *IBM Journal of Research and Development*, **3**, 198–200 (1959).

[S2] SIERPIŃSKI, W., *Cardinal and Ordinal Numbers*. Warsaw, 1958.

The following selected references contain additional material on topics treated in the text.

Chapter 1.

AUFENKAMP, D. D., and F. HOHN, "Analysis of Sequential Machines," *IRE Transactions on Electronic Computers*, **EC6**, 276–285 (1957).

GILL, A., "State-Identification Experiments in Finite Automata," *Information and Control*, **4**, 132–154 (1961).

GILL, A., "Cascaded Finite-State Machines," *IRE Transactions on Electronic Computers*, **EC10**, 366–370 (1961).

HARTMANIS, J., "Symbolic Analysis of a Decomposition of Information Processing Machines," *Information and Control*, **3**, 154–178 (1960).

HUZINO, S., "Theory of Finite Automata," *Memoirs of the Faculty of Sciences, Kyushu University*, Series A, **15**, 95–159 (1962).

SIMON, J., "A Note on Memory Aspects of Sequence Transducers," *IRE Transactions on Circuit Theory*, **CT6**, 26–29 (1959).

YOELI, M., "The Cascade Decomposition of Sequential Machines," *IRE Transactions on Electronic Computers*, **EC10**, 587–592 (1961).

Chapter 2

GINSBURG, S., "Connective Properties Preserved in Minimal State Machines," *Journal of the Association for Computing Machinery*, **7**, 311–325 (1960).

LEE, C. Y., "Automata and Finite Automata," *Bell System Technical Journal*, **39**, 1267–1295 (1960).

RANEY, G. N., "Sequential Functions," *Journal of the Association for Computing Machinery*, **5**, 177–180 (1958).

WANG, H., "Circuit Synthesis by Solving Sequential Boolean Equations," *Zeitschr.f.Math.Logik und Grundlagen d. Math.*, **5**, 291–322 (1959).

Chapter 4

ARBIB, M., "Turing Machines, Finite Automata and Neural Nets," *Journal of the Association for Computing Machinery*, **8**, 467–475 (1961).

BUCHI, J. R., "Regular Canonical Systems and Finite Automata," *Department of Philosophy Technical Report*, University of Michigan, Ann Arbor, Michigan (December 1959).

COPI, J. M., C. C. ELGOT, and J. B. WRIGHT, "Realization of Events by Logical Nets," *Journal of the Association for Computing Machinery*, **5**, 181–196 (1958).

ELGOT, C. C., "Decision Problems of Finite Automata Design and Related Arithmetics," *Transactions of the American Mathematical Society*, **98**, 21–51 (1961).

GLUSKOV, V. M., "Abstract Automata and the Decomposition of Free Semi-groups," *Soviet Mathematics*, Translation of Doklady Academy of Sciences of USSR, **2**, 121–123 (January 1961).

MEDVEDEV, I. T., "On a Class of Events Representable in a Finite Automaton," translated by J. Schorr-Kon, *Lincoln Laboratory Report* 34–73 (June 1958).

OTT, G., and N. H. FEINSTEIN, "Design of Sequential Machines From Their Regular Expressions," *Journal of the Association for Computing Machinery*, **8**, 585–600 (1961).

PERLES, M., M. O. RABIN, and E. SHAMIR, "The Theory of Definite Automata," *Technical Report No. 6*, Applied Logic Branch, The Hebrew University of Jerusalem (August 1961).

SCHUTZENBERGER, M. P., "A Remark on Finite Transducers," *Information and Control*, **4**, 185–196 (1961).

SCHUTZENBERGER, M. P., "On the Definition of a Family of Automata," *Information and Control*, **4**, 245–270 (1961).

APPENDIX

Proof of (b) of Theorem 2.2.

Given $u \leq d$, let $(p_u, q_u) = (z_i, z_j)$. From the construction of δ at stages 2 and 3,

(1) if $k < i$, then $\delta(z_k, I^u) = z_1$; if $i \leq k < j$, then $\delta(z_k, I^u) = \delta(z_i, I^u)$; and if $j \leq k$, then $\delta(z_k, I^u) = \delta(z_j, I^u)$.

Let z_i be a definite state in S. Suppose that $p_j = z_i$. If $j = d$, then $\delta(z_i, I^j) = z_2$. If $j < d$, then either $\delta(z_i, I^j) = z_i$ or $\delta(z_i, I^j) = z_{i+1}$. Suppose that $z_i = q_k$. If $k = d$, then $\delta(z_i, I^k) = z_1$. If $k < d$, then either $\delta(z_i, I^k) = z_{i+1}$ or $i = n$. In any case, if $i \neq n$ and if $\delta(z_i, I) = z_s$ is defined at stage 1, then $s \leq i + 1$. From this it is readily seen that if $i \neq n$ and if $\delta(z_i, I) = z_s$ is defined by the end of stage 2, then $s \leq i + 1$. If $\delta(z_i, I)$ is undefined by the end of stage 2 but is defined at stage 3, then $\delta(z_i, I) = z_1$. Consequently,

(2) if $i \neq n$ and if $\delta(z_i, I) = z_s$, then $s \leq i + 1$.

Consider the tape $J_1 \ldots J_{d+n-1}$ defined by $J_j = I^j$ for $j \leq d$, $J_{d+i} = I^i$ for $i \leq n - 2$, and $J_{d+n-1} = I^{d+1}$. Then

$$\lambda(p_1, J_1 \ldots J_{d+n-1}) = E^1 \ldots E^d \lambda(q_1, J_{d+1} \ldots J_{d+n-1})$$

$$= E^1 \ldots E^d E^1 \ldots E^{n-2} \lambda(q_{n-1}, I^{d+1})$$

$$= E^1 \ldots E^d E^1 \ldots E^{n-2} E^{d+1},$$

the last equality occurring since $q_{n-1} = z_n$. Also,

$$\lambda(q_1, J_1 \ldots J_{d+n-1}) = E^1 \ldots E^d \lambda(p_1, J_{d+1} \ldots J_{d+n-1})$$

$$= E^1 \ldots E^d E^1 \ldots E^{n-2} \lambda(p_n, I^{d+1}),$$

which does not exist since $\lambda(p_n, I^{d+1}) = \lambda(z_{n-1}, I^{d+1})$ is undefined. Thus $p_1 \leq q_1$ is false.

Let t be the smallest integer for which there exists a tape $I_1 \ldots I_t$ which is applicable to p_1 such that either $\lambda(q_1, I_1 \ldots I_t)$ does not exist or else $\lambda(q_1, I_1 \ldots I_t)$ exists but $\lambda(p_1, I_1 \ldots I_t) \neq \lambda(q_1, I_1 \ldots I_t)$. Obviously $t > 1$. From the minimality property of t,

$$\lambda(p_1, I_1 \ldots I_i) = \lambda(q_1, I_1 \ldots I_i) \quad \text{for} \quad i \leq t - 1.$$

Since $\lambda(z_i, I^k) = E^k$ whenever $\lambda(z_i, I^k)$ is defined, it results that for each tape $\bar{I}_1 \ldots \bar{I}_j$, $\lambda(p_1, \bar{I}_1 \ldots \bar{I}_j) = \lambda(q_1, \bar{I}_1 \ldots \bar{I}_j)$ whenever both

$\lambda(p_1, \overline{I}_1 \ldots \overline{I}_j)$ and $\lambda(q_1, \overline{I}_1 \ldots \overline{I}_j)$ exist. Therefore $\lambda(q_1, I_1 \ldots I_t)$ does not exist. Let $u_1 = p_1$, $v_1 = q_1$, and for $i < t$ let $u_{i+1} = \delta(u_i, I_i)$ and $v_{i+1} = \delta(v_i, I_i)$. Since $\lambda(q, I)$ and $\delta(q, I)$ exist together,

$$\delta(u_1, I_1 \ldots I_{t-1}) = u_t \quad \text{and} \quad \delta(v_1, I_1 \ldots I_{t-1})$$

exist. Also, $\delta(u_1, I_1 \ldots I_t) = \delta(u_t, I_t)$ exists. However, $\delta(v_1, I_1 \ldots I_t) = \delta(v_t, I_t)$ does not exist. Thus $u_t \neq v_t$. This implies that

(3) $u_i \neq v_i$ for $i \leq t$.

Suppose that $u_i = u_j$ and $v_i = v_j$ for two integers, i and j, with $i < j \leq t$. Since $\lambda(p_1, I_1 \ldots I_t)$ exists, so does $\lambda(u_j, I_j \ldots I_t)$. Thus

$$\lambda(p_1, I_1 \ldots I_{i-1}I_j \ldots I_t) = \lambda(p_1, I_1 \ldots I_{i-1})\lambda(u_i, I_j \ldots I_t)$$
$$= \lambda(p_1, I_1 \ldots I_{i-1})\lambda(u_j, I_j \ldots I_t)$$

exists. Suppose that $\lambda(q_1, I_1 \ldots I_{i-1}I_j \ldots I_t)$ exists. Then

$$\lambda(v_i, I_j \ldots I_t) = \lambda(v_j, I_j \ldots I_t)$$

exists. Then

$$\lambda(q_1, I_1 \ldots I_t) = \lambda(q_1, I_1 \ldots I_{j-1})\lambda(v_j, I_j \ldots I_t)$$

exists, a contradiction. Hence $\lambda(q_1, I_1 \ldots I_{i-1}I_j \ldots I_t)$ does not exist. Since the tape $I_1 \ldots I_{i-1}I_j \ldots I_t$ is of length less than t, a contradiction of the minimality property of t arises. Therefore,

(4) $(u_i, v_i) \neq (u_j, v_j)$ for $i < j \leq t$.

We now turn to proving that $t = d + n - 1$. Since we have exhibited a tape $J_1 \ldots J_{d+n-1}$ such that $\lambda(p_1, J_1 \ldots J_{d+n-1})$ exists but

$$\lambda(q_1, J_1 \ldots J_{d+n-1})$$

does not, $t \leq d + n - 1$. We shall show that $u_k = p_k$ and $v_k = q_k$ for $k \leq d$, and that $u_{d+i} = q_i$ and $v_{d+i} = p_i$ for $i \leq n - 2$. Then $t \geq d + n - 1$, thus $t = d + n - 1$. Hence $(p_1; q_1; d + n - 2)$ will hold, and the theorem will be proved.

Suppose that $n = 2$. By definition, $u_1 = p_1$ and $v_1 = q_1$. Also, $d + n - 1 = 2$ and $\delta(p_1, I)$ exists only for $I = I^1$. Thus $u_2 = q_1$ and $v_2 = p_1$. Then $t \geq d + n - 1$. Hence $t = d + n - 1$.

Suppose that $n > 2$. By definition, $u_1 = p_1$ and $v_1 = q_1$. Now suppose that $u_k = p_k$ and $v_k = q_k$ for $k \leq w < \min \{d, t\}$, where $\min \{d, t\}$ is the smaller of the numbers d and t. Let $(p_w, q_w) = (z_i, z_j)$, and let $I_w = I^h$. Then $i < j$, since $w < d$. Therefore $i \leq n - 1$. Since $\delta(u_w, I_w) = \delta(z_i, I_w)$ exists and $i \leq n - 1$, it follows that $I_w \neq I^{d+1}$. Thus $h \leq d$. Therefore (p_h, q_h) exists. Let $(p_h, q_h) = (z_r, z_s)$. Several alternatives now arise.

(i) Suppose that $h = w$. Then $p_{w+1} = u_{w+1}$ and $q_{w+1} = v_{w+1}$.

(ii) Suppose that $h < w$. Since $h < w$ and $w < d$, it follows that $h < d$. Thus p_{h+1} and q_{h+1} exist. Since $h < w$, then $r \leq i$. If $r \leq i$, then $r = i < s < j$. If $r < i$, then either $r < i < s < j$, or $r < i < j < s$, or $r < s \leq i < j$. Suppose that $r \leq i < s < j$. Then by (1), $u_{w+1} = \delta(z_i, I^h) = \delta(z_r, I^h) = p_{h+1}$, and $v_{w+1} = \delta(z_j, I^h) = \delta(z_s, I^h) = q_{h+1}$. Since $h + 1 \leq w$ and $(u_k, v_k) = (p_k, q_k)$ for $k \leq w$, $(u_{w+1}, v_{w+1}) = (p_{h+1}, q_{h+1}) = (u_{h+1}, v_{h+1})$. This, combined with $w + 1 \leq t$, contradicts (4). Suppose that $r < i < j < s$. Then $\delta(z_r, I^h) = \delta(z_i, I^h) = \delta(z_j, I^h)$, so that $u_{w+1} = v_{w+1}$. This contradicts (3). Suppose that $r < s \leq i < j$. Then by (1), $\delta(z_s, I^h) = \delta(z_i, I^h)$, so that $u_{w+1} = v_{w+1}$. This also contradicts (3). Thus $h < w$ cannot occur.

(iii) Suppose that $h > w$. Then $i \leq r$. Suppose that $i = r$. Since $h > w$ and $i = r$, then $j < s$. Thus $r = i < j < s$. Then $\delta(z_r, I^h) = \delta(z_i, I^h) = \delta(z_j, I^h)$, that is, $u_{w+1} = v_{w+1}$. This contradicts (3). Now suppose that $i < r$. From the way that δ is defined, $\delta(z_i, I^h)$ is defined at stage three but not at stage two. Thus $u_{w+1} = \delta(z_i, I^h) = z_1$. If $i > 1$, then (u_{w+1}, v_{w+1}) precedes $(u_w, v_w) = (z_i, z_j)$ in C. Thus $(u_{w+1}, v_{w+1}) = (u_k, v_k)$ for some $k < w$, contradicting (4). Suppose that $i = 1$. Since $i < r, h \geq n$. Hence $u_{w+1} = \delta(z_1, I^h) = z_1$. Since $z_1 = z_i, (u_w, v_w) = (z_1, z_j)$. Thus $w = j - 1$. If $j = n$, then

$$(u_{w+1}, v_{w+1}) = (z_1, v_{w+1}) = (p_a, q_a) = (z_1, z_{a+1}) = (u_a, v_a)$$

for some $a \leq n - 1 = w$. This contradicts (4). Suppose that $j < n$. From (2), if $j < n$ and $v_{w+1} = \delta(z_j, I^h) = z_k$, then $k \leq j + 1$, that is, $(u_{w+1}, v_{w+1}) = (z_1, z_k)$, with $k \leq j + 1$. If $k = 1$, then $(u_{w+1}, v_{w+1}) = (z_1, z_1)$, contradicting (3). If $1 < k < j + 1$, then $(u_{w+1}, v_{w+1}) = (z_1, z_k) = (u_{k-1}, v_{k-1})$ with $k - 1 \leq w$, contradicting (4). If $k = j + 1$, then

$$(u_{w+1}, v_{w+1}) = (z_1, z_{j+1}) = (p_{w+1}, q_{w+1}),$$

so that $(u_k, v_k) = (p_k, q_k)$ for $k \leq w + 1$.

Considering all three alternatives, we conclude that $(u_k, v_k) = (p_k, q_k)$ for $k \leq w + 1$. By induction, $(u_k, v_k) = (p_k, q_k)$ for all $k \leq \min \{d, t\}$. Suppose that $t \leq d$. Then $u_t = p_t$ and $v_t = q_t$, with $t \leq d$. Then $u_t \neq z_n$, so that $I_t \neq I^{d+1}$. Therefore $\lambda(u_t, I_t)$, thus $\lambda(v_t, I_t)$ exists, which is a contradiction. Hence $d < t$. Thus $u_d = q_1$ and $v_d = p_1 = z_1$.

By an argument similar to that given in (iii) above, we can show that u_{d+i} and v_{d+i} exist, with $u_{d+i} = q_i$ and $v_{d+i} = p_i = z_1$, for $i \leq n - 2$. Thus $t > d + n - 2$, whence $t = d + n - 1$. This completes the proof of Theorem 2.2.